Math Mammoth
Grade 6-A Worktext

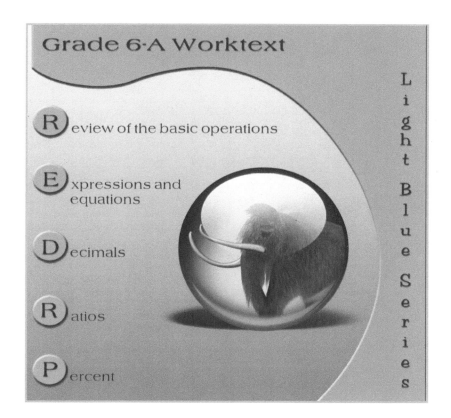

By Maria Miller

Contents

Foreword 5

User Guide 7

Chapter 1: Review of the Basic Operations

Introduction 11

Warm Up: Mental Math 13

Review of the Four Operations 1 15

Review of the Four Operations 2 21

Powers and Exponents 24

Place Value 27

Rounding and Estimating 31

Lessons in Problem Solving 34

Chapter 1 Mixed Review 38

Chapter 1 Review 40

Chapter 2: Expressions and Equations

Introduction 43

The Order of Operations 45

Expressions, Part 1 47

Terminology for the Four Operations 49

Words and Expressions 51

Expressions, Part 2 53

Writing and Simplifying Expressions 1:
Length and Perimeter 55

More on Writing and Simplifying Expressions 58

Writing and Simplifying Expressions 2: Area 61

Multiplying and Dividing in Parts 66

The Distributive Property 70

Equations 74

Solving Equations 76

Writing Equations 80

Inequalities 82

Using Two Variables 86

Chapter 2 Mixed Review 90

Chapter 2 Review 92

Chapter 3: Decimals

Introduction	97
Place Value with Decimals	99
Comparing Decimals	101
Add and Subtract Decimals	103
Rounding Decimals	105
Review: Multiply and Divide Decimals Mentally	108
Review: Multiply Decimals by Decimals	110
Review: Long Division with Decimals	113
Problem Solving with Decimals	115
Fractions and Decimals	117
Multiply and Divide by Powers of Ten	120
Review: Divide Decimals by Decimals	122
Divide Decimals by Decimals 2	125
Convert Customary Measuring Units	127
Convert Metric Measuring Units	131
Convert Between Customary and Metric	134
Chapter 3 Mixed Review	136
Chapter 3 Review	138

Chapter 4: Ratios

Introduction	143
Ratios and Rates	145
Unit Rates	149
Using Equivalent Rates	151
Ratio Problems and Bar Models 1	155
Ratio Problems and Bar Models 2	158
Aspect Ratio	161
Using Ratios to Convert Measuring Units	163
Chapter 4 Mixed Review	167
Chapter 4 Review	169

Chapter 5: Percent

Introduction	171
Percent	173
What Percentage …?	177
Percentage of a Number (Mental Math)	179
Percentage of a Number: Using Decimals	182
Discounts	185
Practice with Percent	187
Finding the Total When the Percentage Is Known	190
Chapter 5 Mixed Review	192
Review: Percent	194

Foreword

Math Mammoth Grade 6 comprises a complete math curriculum for the sixth grade mathematics studies. The curriculum meets and exceeds the Common Core standards.

In sixth grade, we have quite a few topics to study. Some of them, such as fractions and decimals, students are familiar with, but many others are introduced for the first time (e.g. exponents, ratios, percent, integers).

The main areas of study in Math Mammoth Grade 6 are:

- An introduction to several algebraic concepts, such as exponents, expressions, and equations;
- Rational numbers: fractions, decimals, and percents;
- Ratios, rates, and problem solving using bar models;
- Geometry: area, volume, and surface area;
- Integers and graphing;
- Statistics: summarizing distributions using measures of center and variability.

This year starts out, in chapter 1 of part 6-A, with a review of the four operations with whole numbers (including long division), place value, and rounding. Students are also introduced to exponents and do some problem solving.

Chapter 2 starts the study of algebra topics, delving first into expressions and equations. Students practice writing expressions in different ways, and use properties of operations and the idea of maintaining the equality of both sides of an equation to solve simple equations. We also briefly study inequalities and using two variables.

Chapter 3 has to do with decimals. This is a long chapter, as we revise all of decimal arithmetic, just using more decimal digits than in 5th grade Students also convert measuring units in this chapter.

Ratios (chapter 4) is a new topic. Students are already familiar with finding fractional parts, and now it is time to advance that knowledge into the study of ratios, which arise naturally from dividing a quantity into many equal parts. We study such topics as rates, unit rates, equivalent ratios, and problem solving using bar models.

Percent (chapter 5) is an important topic because of its many applications in real life. The goal of this chapter is to develop a basic understanding of percent, to see percentages as decimals, and to learn to calculate discounts.

In part 6-B, students study number theory, fractions, integers, geometry and statistics.

I heartily recommend that you read the full user guide in the following pages.

I wish you success in teaching math!

Maria Miller, the author

User Guide

Note: You can also find the information that follows online, at https://www.mathmammoth.com/userguides/ .

Basic principles in using Math Mammoth Complete Curriculum

Math Mammoth is mastery-based, which means it concentrates on a few major topics at a time, in order to study them in depth. The two books (parts A and B) are like a "framework", but you still have a lot of liberty in planning your child's studies. You can even use it in a *spiral* manner, if you prefer. Simply have your student study in 2-3 chapters simultaneously. In sixth grade, chapters 1 and 2 should be studied before the other chapters, but you can be flexible with all the other chapters and schedule them earlier or later.

Math Mammoth is not a scripted curriculum. In other words, it is not spelling out in exact detail what the teacher is to do or say. Instead, Math Mammoth gives you, the teacher, various tools for teaching:

- **The two student worktexts** (parts A and B) contain all the lesson material and exercises. They include the explanations of the concepts (the teaching part) in blue boxes. The worktexts also contain some advice for the teacher in the "Introduction" of each chapter.

  The teacher can read the teaching part of each lesson before the lesson, or read and study it together with the student in the lesson, or let the student read and study on his own. If you are a classroom teacher, you can copy the examples from the "blue teaching boxes" to the board and go through them on the board.

- There are hundreds of **videos** matched to the curriculum available at https://www.mathmammoth.com/videos/ . There isn't a video for every lesson, but there are dozens of videos for each grade level. You can simply have the author teach your child or student!

- Don't automatically assign all the exercises. Use your judgment, trying to assign just enough for your student's needs. You can use the skipped exercises later for review. For most students, I recommend to start out by assigning about half of the available exercises. Adjust as necessary.

- For each chapter, there is a **link list to various free online games** and activities. These games can be used to supplement the math lessons, for learning math facts, or just for some fun. Each chapter introduction (in the student worktext) contains a link to the list corresponding to that chapter.

- The student books contain some **mixed review lessons**, and the curriculum also provides you with additional **cumulative review lessons**.

- There is a **chapter test** for each chapter of the curriculum, and a comprehensive end-of-year test.

- The **worksheet maker** allows you to make additional worksheets for most calculation-type topics in the curriculum. This is a single html file. You will need Internet access to be able to use it.

- You can use the free online exercises at https://www.mathmammoth.com/practice/ This is an expanding section of the site, so check often to see what new topics we are adding to it!

- Some grade levels have **cut-outs** to make fraction manipulatives or geometric solids.

- And of course there are answer keys to everything.

How to get started

Have ready the first lesson from the student worktext. Go over the first teaching part (within the blue boxes) together with your child. Go through a few of the first exercises together, and then assign some problems for your child to do on their own.

Repeat this if the lesson has other blue teaching boxes. Naturally, you can also use the videos at https://www.mathmammoth.com/videos/

Many children can eventually study the lessons completely on their own — the curriculum becomes self-teaching. However, children definitely vary in how much they need someone to be there to actually teach them.

Pacing the curriculum

The lessons in Math Mammoth complete curriculum are NOT intended to be done in a single teaching session or class. Sometimes you might be able to go through a whole lesson in one day, but more often, the lesson itself might span 3-5 pages and take 2-3 days or classes to complete.

Therefore, it is not possible to say exactly how many pages a student needs to do in one day. This will vary. However, it is helpful to calculate a general guideline as to how many pages per week you should cover in the student worktext in order to go through the curriculum in one school year (or whatever span of time you want to allot to it).

The table below lists how many pages there are for the student to finish in this particular grade level, and gives you a guideline for how many pages per day to finish, assuming a 180-day school year.

Example:

Grade level	Lesson pages	Number of school days	Days for tests and reviews	Days for the student book	Pages to study per day	Pages to study per week
6-A	166	92	10	82	2	10
6-B	157	88	10	78	2	10
Grade 6 total	323	180	20	160	2	10

The table below is for you to fill in. First fill in how many days of school you intend to have. Also allow several days for tests and additional review before the test — at least twice the number of chapters in the curriculum. For example, if the particular grade has 8 chapters, allow at least 16 days for tests & additional review. Then, to get a count of "pages/day", divide the number of pages by the number of available days. Then, multiply this number by 5 to get the approximate page count to cover in a week.

Grade level	Lesson pages	Number of school days	Days for tests and reviews	Days for the student book	Pages to study per day	Pages to study per week
6-A	166					
6-B	157					
Grade 6 total	323					

Now, let's assume you determine that you need to study about 2 pages a day, 10 pages a week in order to get through the curriculum. As you study each lesson, keep in mind that sometimes most of the page might be filled with blue teaching boxes and very few exercises. You might be able to cover 3 pages on such a day. Then some other day you might only assign one page of word problems. Also, you might be able to go through the pages quicker in some chapters, for example when studying graphs, because the large pictures fill the page so that one page does not have many problems.

When you have a page or two filled with lots of similar practice problems ("drill") or large sets of problems, feel free to **only assign 1/2 or 2/3 of those problems**. If your child gets it with less amount of exercises, then that is perfect! If not, you can always assign him/her the rest of the problems some other day. In fact, you could even use these unassigned problems the next week or next month for some additional review.

In general, 1st-2nd graders might spend 25-40 minutes a day on math. Third-fourth graders might spend 30-60 minutes a day. Fifth-sixth graders might spend 45-75 minutes a day. If your child finds math enjoyable, he/she can of course spend more time with it! However, it is not good to drag out the lessons on a regular basis, because that can then affect the child's attitude towards math.

Working space, the usage of additional paper and mental math

The curriculum generally includes working space directly on the page for students to work out the problems. However, feel free to let your students to use extra paper when necessary. They can use it, not only for the "long" algorithms (where you line up numbers to add, subtract, multiply, and divide), but also to draw diagrams and pictures to help organize their thoughts. Some students won't need the additional space (and may resist the thought of extra paper), while some will benefit from it. Use your discretion.

Some exercises don't have any working space, but just an empty line for the answer (e.g. 200 + _____ = 1,000). Typically, I have intended that such exercises to be done using MENTAL MATH.

However, there are some students who struggle with mental math (often this is because of not having studied and used it in the past). As always, the teacher has the final say (not me!) as to how to approach the exercises and how to use the curriculum. We do want to prevent extreme frustration (to the point of tears). The goal is always to provide SOME challenge, but not too much, and to let students experience success enough so that they can continue enjoying learning math.

Students struggling with mental math will probably benefit from studying the basic principles of mental calculations from the earlier levels of Math Mammoth curriculum. To do so, look for lessons that list mental math strategies. They are taught in the chapters about addition, subtraction, place value, multiplication, and division. My article at https://www.mathmammoth.com/lessons/practical_tips_mental_math also gives you a summary of some of those principles.

Using tests

For each chapter, there is a **chapter test**, which can be administered right after studying the chapter. **The tests are optional.** Some families might prefer not to give tests at all. The main reason for the tests is for diagnostic purposes, and for record keeping. These tests are not aligned or matched to any standards.

In the digital version of the curriculum, the tests are provided both as PDF files and as html files. Normally, you would use the PDF files. The html files are included so you can edit them (in a word processor such as Word or LibreOffice), in case you want your student to take the test a second time. Remember to save the edited file under a different file name, or you will lose the original.

The end-of-year test is best administered as a diagnostic or assessment test, which will tell you how well the student remembers and has mastered the mathematics content of the entire grade level.

Using cumulative reviews and the worksheet maker

The student books contain mixed review lessons which review concepts from earlier chapters. The curriculum also comes with additional cumulative review lessons, which are just like the mixed review lessons in the student books, with a mix of problems covering various topics. These are found in their own folder in the digital version, and in the Tests & Cumulative Reviews book in the print version.

The cumulative reviews are optional; use them as needed. They are named indicating which chapters of the main curriculum the problems in the review come from. For example, "Cumulative Review, Chapter 4" includes problems that cover topics from chapters 1-4.

Both the mixed and cumulative reviews allow you to spot areas that the student has not grasped well or has forgotten. When you find such a topic or concept, you have several options:

1. Check if the worksheet maker lets you make worksheets for that topic.

2. Check for any online games and resources in the Introduction part of the particular chapter in which this topic or concept was taught.

3. If you have the digital version, you could simply reprint the lesson from the student worktext, and have the student restudy that.

4. Perhaps you only assigned 1/2 or 2/3 of the exercise sets in the student book at first, and can now use the remaining exercises.

5. Check if our online practice area at https://www.mathmammoth.com/practice/ has something for that topic.

6. Khan Academy has free online exercises, articles, and videos for most any math topic imaginable.

Concerning challenging word problems and puzzles

While this is not absolutely necessary, I heartily recommend supplementing Math Mammoth with challenging word problems and puzzles. You could do that once a month, for example, or more often if the student enjoys it.

The goal of challenging story problems and puzzles is to **develop the student's logical and abstract thinking and mental discipline**. I recommend starting these in fourth grade, at the latest. Then, students are able to read the problems on their own and have developed mathematical knowledge in many different areas. Of course I am not discouraging students from doing such in earlier grades, either.

Math Mammoth curriculum contains lots of word problems, and they are usually multi-step problems. Several of the lessons utilize a bar model for solving problems. Even so, the problems I have created are usually tied to a specific concept or concepts. I feel students can benefit from solving problems and puzzles that require them to think "out of the box" or are just different from the ones I have written.

I recommend you use the free Math Stars problem-solving newsletters as one of the main resources for puzzles and challenging problems:

Math Stars Problem Solving Newsletter (grades 1-8)
https://www.homeschoolmath.net/teaching/math-stars.php

I have also compiled a list of other resources for problem solving practice, which you can access at this link:

https://l.mathmammoth.com/challengingproblems

Another idea: you can find puzzles online by searching for "brain puzzles for kids," "logic puzzles for kids" or "brain teasers for kids."

Frequently asked questions and contacting us

If you have more questions, please first check the FAQ at https://www.mathmammoth.com/faq-lightblue

If the FAQ does not cover your question, you can then contact us using the contact form at the Math Mammoth.com website.

Chapter 1: Review of the Basic Operations
Introduction

The goal of the first chapter in year 6 is to review the four basic operations with whole numbers, place value and rounding, as well as to learn about exponents and problem solving.

A lot of this chapter is review, and I hope this provides a gentle start for 6th year math. In the next chapter, we will then delve into some beginning algebra topics.

Special notes for this chapter: problem solving

This chapter doesn't have many new concepts – only the concept of exponents and powers. Besides reviewing how to perform the four basic operations with pencil and paper, students also get some practice for problem solving.

Solving (word) problems in math works much the same way as solving problems in real life. You may start out one way, come to a "dead end", and have to take an entirely different approach. Good problem solvers monitor their progress as they work, and change course if necessary.

Here is a list of general tips and strategies for solving mathematical problems that you can share with your student(s).

- If you cannot solve the original problem, try to **solve an easier, related problem first**. This may help you find a way to solve the original. For example, if the numbers in the problem seem intimidating, change them temporarily to really easy numbers and see if you can solve the problem then. Or reduce the details mentioned in the problem to make it simpler, solve the simpler problem, then go back to the original. You can also try special cases of the problem at hand at first.

- Drawing a sketch, a diagram (e.g. a bar model), or making a table can be very helpful.

- **Check your final answer** if at all possible, using a different method. For example, division problems can be checked by multiplication and subtractions by addition. Multi-step problems can often be solved in different ways or in a different order.

  At the very least, **check that your answer is reasonable** and actually makes sense. If the problem is asking how many days of vacation someone might get in a year, and you get an answer in the thousands, you can tell something went really wrong. And, once you find your answer is wrong – maybe it doesn't make sense – it is NOT time to cry and give up. Do you know how many times Thomas Alva Edison tried and failed, until he finally found a way to make a commercially viable electric light bulb? Thousands of times.

  Perseverance is something that is very necessary when you encounter problems in real life, and I don't mean math problems. Everyone fails, but it is those who keep trying who will ultimately succeed. Every successful entrepreneur can tell you that. Failing is *not* a sign of being stupid. It is a sign of being a human. ALL of us make mistakes and fail. ALL of us improve as we keep trying.

- Often, it is easier and neater to perform paper-and-pen calculations (long addition, subtraction, multiplication, division) on a grid paper.

- The space in the worktext may not be enough. Use as much scrap paper (extra paper) as necessary.

- Remember to include a unit (if applicable) in the answers to word problems.

General principles in using the curriculum

Please note that it is not recommended to assign all the exercises by default. Use your judgment, and strive to vary the number of assigned exercises according to the student's needs.

The specific lessons in the chapter can take several days to finish. They are not "daily lessons." Instead, use the general guideline that sixth graders should finish about two pages daily or 10 pages a week in order to finish the curriculum in about 36 weeks.

See the user guide at in the beginning of this book or online at **https://www.mathmammoth.com/userguides/** for more guidance on using and pacing the curriculum.

The Lessons in Chapter 1

	page	span
Warm-Up: Mental Math	13	*2 pages*
Review of the Four Operations 1	15	*6 pages*
Review of the Four Operations 2	21	*3 pages*
Powers and Exponents	24	*3 pages*
Place Value	27	*4 pages*
Rounding and Estimating	31	*3 pages*
Lessons in Problem Solving	34	*4 pages*
Chapter 1 Mixed Review	38	*2 pages*
Chapter 1 Review	40	*2 pages*

Helpful Resources on the Internet

We have compiled a list of Internet resources that match the topics in this chapter. This list of links includes web pages that offer:

- **online practice** for concepts;
- online **games**, or occasionally, printable games;
- **animations** and interactive **illustrations** of math concepts;
- **articles** that teach a math concept.

We heartily recommend you take a look at the list. Many of our customers love using these resources to supplement the bookwork. You can use the resources as you see fit for extra practice, to illustrate a concept better and even just for some fun. Enjoy!

https://l.mathmammoth.com/gr6ch1

SCAN ME

Warm-up: Mental Math

To **multiply** 2,000 × 120, simply multiply 2 × 12, and place four zeros on the end of the answer:

$$2,000 \times 120 = 240,000$$

Solve **division** by thinking of multiplication "backwards":

$$5,600 \div 70 = ?$$

Think what number times 70 will give you 5,600.
Since 70 × 80 = 5,600,
then 5,600 ÷ 70 = 80.

You can **add in parts**.

$$76 + 120 + 65 = ?$$

First add 70 + 120 + 60 = 250.
Then, 6 + 5 = 11.
Lastly, 250 + 11 = 261.

The **order of operations** is:
1. Parentheses 2. Exponents; 3. Multiplication and division; 4. Addition and subtraction.

To calculate 9 × 80 − 10 × 70, first solve 9 × 80 and 10 × 70 . Subtract only after those calculations.

$$9 \times 80 \ - \ 10 \times 70$$

$$= \ 720 \ - \ 700 \ = \ 20$$

In the expression 4,500 ÷ (5 + 45) × 80, solve 5 + 45 first. Then, divide.

$$4,500 \div (5 + 45) \times 80$$

$$= 4,500 \div 50 \times 80$$

$$= 90 \times 80 = 7,200$$

---

1. Solve in your head.

a. $410 + 2 \times 19$ =	**b.** $3 \times 50 + 4 \times 150$ =	**c.** $70 \times 80 - 40 \times 50$ =
d. $14 + (530 - 440)$ =	**e.** $45 + 56 + 35$ =	**f.** $300 \div 5 - 400 \div 10$ =

2. Solve in your head.

a. $17 + \underline{\hspace{2cm}} = 110$ **b.** $345 + \underline{\hspace{2.5cm}} = 1,000$ **c.** $3 \times 40 + \underline{\hspace{2.5cm}} = 500$

3. Divide. Remember that division can also be written using a fraction line.

a. $\dfrac{240}{4} =$ **c.** $\dfrac{72}{9} =$ **e.** $\dfrac{5,600}{10} =$ **g.** $\dfrac{420}{20} =$ **i.** $\dfrac{420}{70} =$

b. $\dfrac{7,200}{100} =$ **d.** $\dfrac{450}{9} =$ **f.** $\dfrac{8,000}{200} =$ **h.** $\dfrac{10,000}{50} =$ **j.** $\dfrac{7,200}{800} =$

4. Solve. Notice carefully which operation(s) are done first.

a. $500 - 40 - 3 \times 50 =$ _____	**b.** $1{,}020 - (40 - 10) \times 20 =$ _____
c. $42{,}000 - 12{,}000 + 3 \times 5{,}000 =$ _____	**d.** $(70 - 20) \times 70 =$ _____
e. $\dfrac{210}{2} + 3 \times 15 =$ _____	**f.** $250 \times 4 + \dfrac{6{,}300}{70} =$ _____

5. Find a number that fits in place of the unknown.

a. $x \div 70 = 40$	**b.** $20 \times M = 1{,}200$	**c.** $500 - y = 320$

6. Find the rule that is used in the table and fill in the missing numbers.

n	130	250	360	410	775	820	1,000
$n -$ ____		215		375			

7. Find the rule that is used in the table and fill in the missing numbers.

n	3	5	12	15	25	35	60
		200			1,000		

8. Rick cut off a 50-cm piece from a 6-meter board, and then he divided the rest of the board into five equal pieces. How long was each piece?

9. **a.** Evelyn works 8 hours a day and earns $104 daily. What is her hourly wage?

   b. How much does Evelyn earn in a five-day work week?

   How much does she earn in three months (which is 13 weeks)?
   (You may use paper and pencil for this one.)

10. Alexis and Mia baked biscuits for a bake sale. They used this recipe, but they needed to triple it:

   a. Triple the recipe for them.

   b. How many biscuits did they bake?

   2 1/4 cups of flour
   3 teaspoons of baking powder
   1/3 cup of honey
   1/2 cup of butter
   3/4 teaspoon of nutmeg
   1 1/2 teaspoons of cinnamon
   1/2 teaspoon of ground cloves
   3/4 cup of walnuts
   Makes 2 1/2 dozen biscuits.

Review of the Four Operations 1

1. Use the following problems to review long division and multiplication.

a.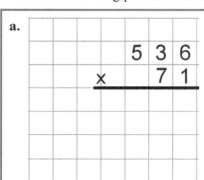

```
    5 3 6
  x    7 1
```

b.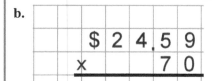

```
  $ 2 4 . 5 9
  x        7 0
```

c.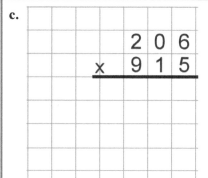

```
    2 0 6
  x  9 1 5
```

d.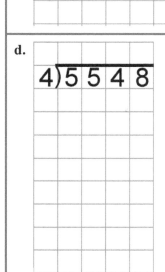

```
4)5 5 4 8
```

e.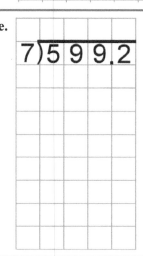

```
7)5 9 9.2
```

f.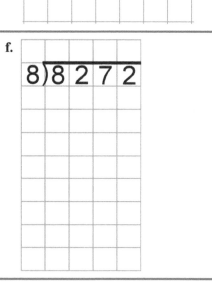

```
8)8 2 7 2
```

2. How do you check the result of *any* division problem? *(Hint: check the next page.)*

Now, check your answers for 1. d, 1. e and 1. f.

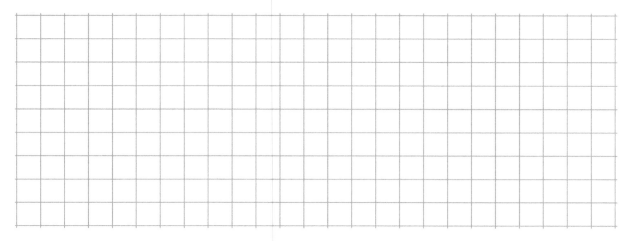

```
      1 3                1 3 3              1 3 3 5            1 3 3 5 4 9
6)8 0 1 2 9 8      6)8 0 1 2 9 8      6)8 0 1 2 9 8      6)8 0 1 2 9 8
 -6                 -6                 -6                 -6
  2 0                2 0                2 0                2 0
 -1 8               -1 8               -1 8               -1 8
    2                 2 1                2 1                2 1
                    -1 8               -1 8               -1 8
                       3                3 2                3 2
                                       -3 0               -3 0
                                        2 9                2 9
                                                          -2 4
                                                           5 8
                                                          -5 4
                                                             4
```

Long division works the same way when there are several digits in the dividend (the big number we divide into). Study the example carefully.

The answer we get is 801,298 ÷ 6 = 133,549 R4.

3. Divide using long division.

a.

```
7)4 2 3 3 6
```

b.
```
6)2 0 9.7 0
```

c.
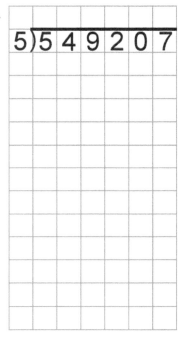
```
5)5 4 9 2 0 7
```

To check a division result that has a remainder, multiply the result by the divisor, and then *add* the remainder. You should get the original dividend.

In this case, we multiply and add: 6 × 133,549 + 4 = 801,298, so it checks.

Remember that <u>the remainder is always less than the divisor</u>; if it isn't, you can continue the division!

4. Check each division by multiplying and adding. If the division is incorrect, correct it.

a. 437 ÷ 6 = 72 R5	**b.** 2,045 ÷ 3 = 681 R1
_____ × _____ + _____ =	_____ × _____ + _____ =

5. A bakery bagged 177 buns into bags of eight, getting 21 bags, and nine buns left over. The division was: $177 \div 8 = 21$ R9. Jessica *immediately* spotted this was wrong (without calculating anything). How did she do that?

6. A large school has 542 sixth graders. How would you divide them into classes as evenly as possible, with about 25 students per class?

7. Divide, using two-digit divisors. You can build a multiplication table for the divisor to help you. Lastly, check your result.

$2 \times 45 = 90$	**a.** $45\overline{)4\ 0\ 0\ 5}$	$\begin{array}{r} \times\ \ 4\ 5 \\ \hline \end{array}$
$2 \times 75 = 150$	**b.** $75\overline{)1\ 9.8\ 7\ 5}$	$\begin{array}{r} \times\ \ 7\ 5 \\ \hline \end{array}$

8. Divide, using two-digit divisors. These may have a remainder. You can build a multiplication table for the divisor to help you. Lastly, check your result.

$2 \times 48 = 96$	a. $48 \overline{)8\ 7\ 0\ 2\ 5}$	$\begin{array}{r} \times\ \ 4\ \ 8 \\ \hline \end{array}$
$2 \times 90 = 180$	b. $90 \overline{)8\ 7\ 1\ 6\ 6\ 0}$	$\begin{array}{r} \times\ \ 9\ \ 0 \\ \hline \end{array}$
$2 \times 82 = 164$	c. $82 \overline{)5\ 4\ 0\ 2\ 2}$	$\begin{array}{r} \times\ \ 8\ \ 2 \\ \hline \end{array}$

9. Try your division skills with 3-digit divisors, too. The answer key has the complete solution, if you get "stuck."

	a. $101\overline{)299046}$	$\begin{array}{r} \times\ 1\ 0\ 1 \\ \hline \end{array}$
	b. $123\overline{)3634206}$	$\begin{array}{r} \times\ 1\ 2\ 3 \\ \hline \end{array}$
	c. $350\overline{)7652000}$	$\begin{array}{r} \times\ 3\ 5\ 0 \\ \hline \end{array}$

10. Here are some riddles for you to solve for more practice with long division! Use your notebook.

I	42,408 ÷ 76	**E**	44,217 ÷ 51	**E**	128,316 ÷ 111
M	85,104 ÷ 54	**I**	223,496 ÷ 91	**E**	51,313 ÷ 97
O	23,530 ÷ 26	**I**	30,624 ÷ 33	**M**	880,341 ÷ 309
R	61,880 ÷ 35	**R**	133,140 ÷ 70	**T**	113,168 ÷ 88
V	51,944 ÷ 86	**S**	11,880 ÷ 22	**R**	693,360 ÷ 810

What is as round as a dishpan, and no matter the size, all the water in the ocean cannot fill it up?

540   558   529   604   1,156

What flies without wings?

1,286   928   1,576   867

I am the only thing that always tells the truth. I show off everything that I see.

2,849   2,456   1,768   1,902   905   856

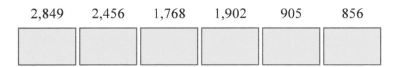

G	200,196 ÷ 201	**R**	617,105 ÷ 415	**O**	1,388,740 ÷ 230
O	324,729 ÷ 57	**S**	2,863,250 ÷ 250	**P**	759,290 ÷ 70
E	339,388 ÷ 31	**T**	1,049,664 ÷ 88	**I**	678,040 ÷ 506
S	2,337,820 ÷ 205	**H**	236,215 ÷ 35	**T**	250,536 ÷ 44
E	28,548 ÷ 18	**F**	97,920 ÷ 16	**F**	239,397 ÷ 199

From what heavy seven-letter word can you take away two letters and have eight left?

1,203   1,487   1,586   1,340   996   6,749   5,694

The more of them you take, the more you leave behind. What are they?

6,120   6,038   5,697   11,928   11,453   11,928   10,948   10,847   11,404

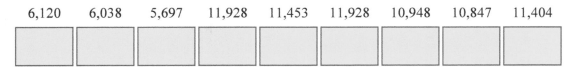

Review of the Four Operations 2

1. Last year, in the Gordon family, Father earned $29,600, Mother earned $13,500, and Matt earned $8,300. They figured out that they had paid about 1/5 of their total earnings in taxes, and used about 1/4 of their income for groceries.

   a. Calculate how much the family used for groceries.

   b. What fractional part of their income did the family have left to spend, after taxes and groceries?

2. Find the value of these expressions, using paper and pencil methods. Use your notebook for more space.

   a. $100 - 29.5 \times 2.6$

   b. $2.3 + 9.356 + 0.403 + 908.8$

   c. $800 - (12.48 - 2.9)$

   d. $559.50 \div 3$

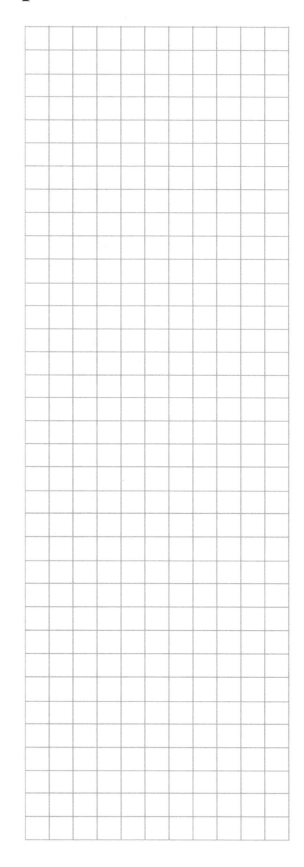

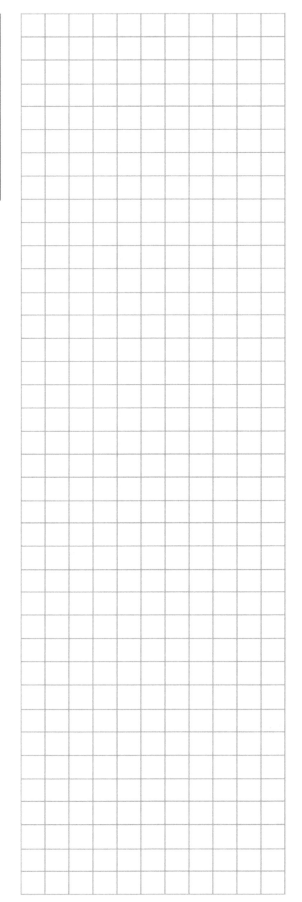

Problem solving hints

- If you cannot solve the problem at hand, think: what *can* you solve? Solve *something* about the situation. Once you find that out, it might help you find a way to solve the entire problem.

- You can change the problem to a similar, easier problem and try to solve that first. For example, you can change the numbers to easier numbers, or drop some of the details to solve a part of the problem.

3. Write the division equation, if the calculation to check it is $13 \times 381 + 5 = 4{,}958$.

4. **a.** If you need to solve $65 \div 7$ to three decimal digits using long division, how many decimal zeros should you add to 65 before starting the division?

   b. Solve $65 \div 7$ to three decimal digits.

5. A large gym floor measures 10 m by 12 m. The teacher divides that into nine equal-sized areas. How big is each area in square meters? Give your answer to two decimal digits.

6. An apple harvest produced 2,350 kg of apples. The farmer packed 36 apples per box. One apple weighs approximately 250 grams. How many boxes were needed to pack the apples?

7. **a.** A car is traveling at 54 miles per hour. Fill in the table:

Miles				54 Miles			
Time	10 min	20 min	30 min	1 hour	2 hours	2 1/2 hours	3 hours

  b. If the Jones family travels steadily at 54 miles per hour, how far will they travel in 9 hours?

  c. *Estimate* how many *hours* it takes them to travel 550 miles.

8. Dad drives at a constant speed of 40 miles per hour.

  a. How many minutes does it take him to travel 5 miles?

  b. How about 100 miles?

  c. Dad drives 30 miles to work. What time should he leave to arrive at exactly 9:00 am?

9. A company bought 96 gallons of fruit juice for a total of $3,072. They packaged it into 8-ounce bottles.

  a. How many jars did they fill?

> *Think:* how many ounces are in a gallon?

  b. What is the minimum price that they would have to charge per bottle to get back at least what they paid ("break even")?

Puzzle Corner   Find what is missing from the equations. You do *not* need to calculate anything!

a. $4{,}392 - \underline{} + 293 = 4{,}392$

b. $384 \div 8 \times \underline{} = 384$

c. $\dfrac{1{,}568}{49} \times \underline{} = 1{,}568$

Powers and Exponents

Exponents are a "shorthand" for writing repeated multiplications by the same number.

For example, $2 \times 2 \times 2 \times 2 \times 2$ is written 2^5.
$5 \times 5 \times 5 \times 5 \times 5 \times 5$ is written 5^6.

The tiny raised number is called the **exponent**. It tells us how many times the *base* number is multiplied by itself.

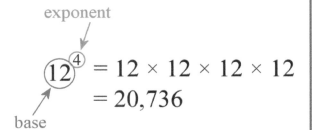

$$12^4 = 12 \times 12 \times 12 \times 12 = 20,736$$

The expression 2^5 is read as "two to the fifth power," "two to the fifth," or "two raised to the fifth power."

Similarly, 7^9 is read as "seven to the ninth power," "seven to the ninth," or "seven raised to the ninth power."

The "powers of 6" are simply expressions where 6 is raised to some power: For example, 6^3, 6^4, 6^{45} and 6^{99} are powers of 6. What would powers of 10 be?

Expressions with the exponent 2 are usually read as something "**squared.**" For example, 11^2 is read as "**eleven squared.**" That is because it gives us *the area of a square* with the side length of 11 units.

Similarly, if the exponent is 3, the expression is usually read using the word "**cubed.**" For example, 31^3 is read as "**thirty-one cubed**" because it gives the *volume of a cube* with the edge length of 31 units.

1. Write the expressions as multiplications, and then solve them in your head.

   a. $3^2 = \underline{3 \times 3 = 9}$ **b.** 1^6

   c. 4^3 **d.** 10^4

   e. 5^3 **f.** 10^2

   g. 2^3 **h.** 8^2

   i. 0^5 **j.** 10^5

   k. 50^2 **l.** 100^3

2. Rewrite the expressions using an exponent, then solve them. You may use a calculator.

   a. $2 \times 2 \times 2 \times 2 \times 2 \times 2$ **b.** $8 \times 8 \times 8 \times 8 \times 8$

   c. 40 squared   **d.** $10 \times 10 \times 10 \times 10$

   e. nine to the eighth power   **f.** eleven cubed

You just learned that the expression 7^2 is read "seven *squared*" because it tells us the area of a *square* with a side length of 7 units. Let's compare that to square meters and other units of area.

If the sides of a square are 3 m long, then its area is 3 m × 3 m = 9 m² or nine square meters.

Notice that the symbol for square meters is **m²**. This means "**meter × meter**." We are, in effect, squaring the unit *meter* (multiplying the unit of length *meter* by itself)!

The expression (9 cm)² means 9 cm × 9 cm. We multiply 9 by itself, but we also multiply the unit *cm* by itself. That is why the result is **81 cm²**. The square centimeter (cm²) comes from multiplying "**centimeter × centimeter**."

We do the same thing with any other unit of length to form the corresponding unit for area, such as square kilometers or square millimeters.

In a similar way, to calculate the volume of this cube, we multiply 5 m × 5 m × 5 m = 125 m³. We not only multiply 5 by itself three times, but also multiply the unit *meter* by itself three times (meter × meter × meter) to get the unit of volume "cubic meter" or m³.

3. Express the area (A) as a multiplication, and solve.

a. A square with a side of 12 kilometers: A = ___12 km × 12 km___ = _____	**b.** A square with sides 6 m long: A = _____
c. A square with a side length of 6 centimeters: A = _____	**d.** A square with a side with a length of 12 cm: A = _____

4. Express the volume (V) as a multiplication, and solve.

a. A cube with an edge of 2 cm: V = _2 cm × 2 cm × 2 cm_ = _____	**b.** A cube with edges 10 cm long each: V = _____
c. A cube with edges 1 m in length: V = _____	**d.** A cube with edges that are all 5 m long: V = _____

5. **a.** The perimeter of a square is 40 centimeters. What is its area?

   b. The volume of a cube is 64 cubic centimeters. How long is its edge?

   c. The area of a square is 121 m². What is its perimeter?

   d. The volume of a cube is 27 cm³. What is the length of one edge?

The powers of 10 are very special —and very easy!	$10^1 = 10$	$10^4 = 10,000$
	$10^2 = 10 \times 10 = 100$	$10^5 = 100,000$
Notice that the exponent tells us *how many zeros* there are in the answer.	$10^3 = 10 \times 10 \times 10 = 1,000$	$10^6 = 1,000,000$

6. Fill in the patterns. In part (d), choose your own number to be the base.
   Use a calculator in parts (c) and (d).

a.	b.	c.	d.
$2^1 =$	$3^1 =$	$5^1 =$	
$2^2 =$	$3^2 =$	$5^2 =$	
$2^3 =$	$3^3 =$	$5^3 =$	
$2^4 =$	$3^4 =$	$5^4 =$	
$2^5 =$	$3^5 =$	$5^5 =$	
$2^6 =$	$3^6 =$	$5^6 =$	

7. Look at the patterns above. Think carefully how each step comes from the previous one. Then answer.

   a. If $3^7 = 2,187$, how can you use that result to find 3^8?

   b. Now find 3^8 without a calculator.

   c. If $2^{45} = 35,184,372,088,832$, use that to find 2^{46} without a calculator.

8. Fill in.

   a. 17^2 gives us the _____ of a _____ with sides _____ units long.

   b. 101^3 gives us the _____ of a _____ with edges _____ units long.

   c. 2×6^2 gives us the _____ of two _____ with sides _____ units long.

   d. 4×10^3 gives us the _____ of ____ _____ with edges _____ units long.

Make a pattern, called a **sequence**, with the powers of 2, starting with 2^6 and going *backwards* to 2^0. At each step, *divide* by 2. What is the logical (though surprising) value for 2^0 from this method?

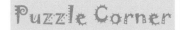

Make another, similar, sequence for the powers of 10. Start with 10^6 and divide by 10 until you reach 10^0. What value do you calculate for 10^0?

Try this same pattern for at least one other base number, n. What value do you calculate for n^0?
Do you think it will come out this way for every base number?

Why or why not?

Place Value

h	t	o	h	t	o	h	t	o	h	t	o	h	t	o
2	0	9	3	5	6	0	7	5	8	5	5	4	0	2

trillions period	billions period	millions period	thousands period	ones period

The letters "h t o" stand for hundreds, tens, ones.

Read this number as:

"Two hundred nine trillion, three hundred fifty-six billion, seventy-five million, eight hundred fifty-five thousand, four hundred and two."

To write this number in its *expanded form*, take each digit's value, and write them all as a sum:

200,000,000,000,000 + 9,000,000,000,000 + 300,000,000,000 + 50,000,000,000 + 6,000,000,000 + 70,000,000 + 5,000,000 + 800,000 + 50,000 + 5,000 + 400 + 2

This is easier to write using exponents:

2×10^{14} + 9×10^{12} + 3×10^{11} + 5×10^{10} + 6×10^9

+ 7×10^7 + 5×10^6 + 8×10^5 + 5×10^4 + 5×10^3 + 4×10^2 + 2×10^0

Remember that in powers of 10, the exponent tells you how many zeros are in the number. For example, 10^{11} = 100,000,000,000 has eleven zeros. Notice especially: **$10^0 = 1$** (the number 1 has no zeros!).

The number system we use is based on *place value*. This means that a digit's *value* depends on its position or *place* within the number.

Our number system is called a *decimal*, or *base-ten*, system (from the Latin word `decima`, *a tenth part*). The value of each position or place is <u>one-tenth</u> of the value of the previous place.

h	t	o	h	t	o	h	t	o	h	t	o	h	t	o
0	0	0	6	3	0	9	5	7	8	1	2	4	9	8

trillions period	billions period	millions period	thousands period	ones period

The digit "6" is in the hundred billions place. Its value is 6 × a hundred billion, or 600 billion.

The digit "5" is in the ten millions place. Its value is 5 × ten million, or 50 million.

1. Write the numbers in the place value chart. Answer the questions.

a. 89 million, 2 thousand, 4 hundred

What is the value of the digit "9"?

_____

trillions period	billions period	millions period	thousands period	ones period

b. 142 billion, 2 million, 139 thousand

What is the value of the digit "3"?

_____

trillions period	billions period	millions period	thousands period	ones period

c. 5 trillion, 47 million, 260

What is the value of the digit "4"?

_____

trillions period	billions period	millions period	thousands period	ones period

2. What is the place and the value of the digit 8 in the following numbers?

a. 56,809	b. 287,403,222	c. 18,503,200,000,000	d. 8,493,591,000
the hundreds place	_____	_____	_____
value _800_	value _____	value _____	value _____

3. Write as numbers.

   a. 2 billion, 180 million, 27 thousand

   b. 60 trillion, 453 thousand

   c. 4 trillion, 50 billion, 54 million, 9

4. Write the numbers and their names corresponding to the powers of ten. Notice especially that $10^0 = 1$.

10^0	1	one
10^1	10	ten
10^2		
10^3	1,000	one thousand
10^4		
10^5		
10^6		
10^7		ten million
10^8		
10^9		
10^{10}		
10^{11}		
10^{12}		

5. Write in normal form (as a number).

a. $8 \times 10^4 + 5 \times 10^2 + 7 \times 10^0$	b. $7 \times 10^6 + 5 \times 10^4 + 6 \times 10^3 + 6 \times 10^1$
c. $7 \times 10^9 + 1 \times 10^8 + 7 \times 10^7$	d. $6 \times 10^8 + 4 \times 10^6 + 5 \times 10^5 + 1 \times 10^4 + 2 \times 10^3$
e. $2 \times 10^9 + 3 \times 10^8 + 5 \times 10^6 + 8 \times 10^5 + 7 \times 10^4$	f. $6 \times 10^4 + 2 \times 10^7 + 1 \times 10^5 + 2 \times 10^0$

6. Write in expanded form, in two ways. Look at the model.

a. $2,839 = 2,000 + 800 + 30 + 9$ $= 2 \times 10^3 + 8 \times 10^2 + 3 \times 10^1 + 9 \times 10^0$	**b.** 483
c. 10,540	
d. 407,000	
e. 500,120,000	
f. 4,078,003	

7. Compare and write < , > or =.

a. a million ☐ 10^5 **b.** 450,000 ☐ 10^6 **c.** 10^9 ☐ a billion

d. $10^5 - 100$ ☐ 10^4 **e.** $10^3 + 10^2$ ☐ 10^4 **f.** 5×10^4 ☐ 4×10^5

g. 3×10^4 ☐ thirty thousand   **h.** $10^8 + 10^7$ ☐ 10^9 **i.** 1×10^8 ☐ 9×10^7

8. Continue the patterns for six more numbers.

a. 1,300,000; 1,400,000; 1,500,000;

b. 724,388; 724,588; 724,788;

c. 15,100,000; 15,500,000; 15,900,000

9. Write in order from the smallest to the largest.

a. 10^8 109,000 8,000,000	**b.** 7×10^9 9×10^7 970,000,000
c. 54,050 450,055 450,540	**d.** 8,999,000 8,998,998 8×10^6
e. 5×10^5 45,005 55,400	**f.** 7×10^6 6×10^7 700,000

10. Calculate without a calculator (using mental math and paper and pencil).

   a. $10^6 - 10^4 + 50,000$

   b. $295,209,328 - 7,399,800 - 25,906$

   c. $5 \times 10^6 + 456,200 + 8 \times 10^9$

11. Subtract 1, 10, 100, or 1,000. Be careful!

Number	10,000	350,000	1,200,000	74,900	203,060
−1					
− 10					
− 100					
− 1,000					

12. China's population in 2020 (November) was about 1,412,800,000. This was expected to grow by 8,331,000 people during 2021, and by another 8,380,000 during 2022.

   a. Estimate China's population at the end of 2022 to the nearest million.

   b. The population of Canada was estimated at about 38,346,000 (July 2021), and of Honduras at 9,451,000 (July 2021). Use mental math. *Approximately* how many times more was the population of Canada than of Honduras?

Rounding and Estimating

You have already learned a lot about rounding in the previous years, so this lesson is just a review.

Rounding rules remain the same no matter what place you are rounding to.

1. Find the digit you are rounding to.

2. Look at the digit AFTER that digit.
   - If that digit is 0, 1, 2, 3, or 4, then round down.
   - If that digit is 5, 6, 7, 8, or 9, then round up.

3. If rounding down, the digit in the place you are rounding to does not change.

4. If rounding up, the digit in the place you are rounding to increases by 1.

5. The digits *after* the place you are rounding to will be replaced by zeros.

You can draw a line right after the digit you are rounding to:

$12{,}7{|}51{,}236 \approx 12{,}800{,}000$ $\qquad$ $5{,}37{|}1{,}891{,}000 \approx 5{,}370{,}000{,}000$

About nines: when rounding up, sometimes you need to increase the digit 9 by one. It becomes 10—but that means you have to *carry* (regroup) the increase to the digit in the *next higher* place. The digit in the next higher place increases by 1, and the digit in the place you are rounding to simply becomes zero.

$2{,}9{|}81{,}391 \approx 3{,}000{,}000$ $\qquad$ $79{|}608{,}000 \approx 80{,}000{,}000$

There may also be several nines in a row, in which case they all become zeros, and the first non-nine digit is increased by 1:

$79{,}9{|}56 \approx 80{,}000$ $\qquad$ $349{,}999{|},812{,}348 \approx 350{,}000{,}000{,}000$

If you have only nines, they all become zeros, except the leading nine in the "front" becomes 10:

$99{,}9{|}79{,}290 \approx 100{,}000{,}000$ $\qquad$ $999{,}99{|}6{,}819 \approx 1{,}000{,}000{,}000$

---

1. Round to the nearest...

Number	410,987	699,893	12,781,284	3,259,949	1,495,397
...thousand					
...ten thousand					
...hundred thousand					
...million					

2. Round to the nearest...

Number	8,419,289,387	12,238,994,038	3,459,994,920	2,203,845,108
...ten million				
...hundred million				
...billion				

3. Round to the place of the underlined digit. Be careful with the nines!

a. $29\underline{9},724 \approx$ _____

b. $1,399,\underline{9}56 \approx$ _____

c. $698,99\underline{9},865 \approx$ _____

d. $499,\underline{9}98,325 \approx$ _____

To estimate, round the numbers in such a way that *you* can calculate the estimate in your head, depending on your mental math skills. Often this means rounding the numbers to the largest place. Compare the two estimates below.

Estimate 1	**Estimate 2**
$27 \times 3,910$	$27 \times 3,910$
$\approx 30 \times 4,000 = 120,000$	$\approx 25 \times 4,000 = 100,000$
Both numbers are rounded to the largest place they have (tens; thousands). The multiplication is easy (essentially a single-digit multiplication of 3×4).	Since 3,910 is rounded up, we round 27 *down* to 25. This will lessen the error of estimation in a *multiplication* problem. However, that would not happen with a subtraction or division.

4. Estimate the result using mental math and rounded numbers. Then find the exact value using a calculator. Lastly, find the error of estimation, which is the difference between your estimate and the exact answer.

a. $2,384 \times 19,384$	**b.** $345 \times 61,852$
Estimation:	Estimation:
Exact:	Exact:
Error of estimation:	Error of estimation:
c. $124,012 - 16 \times 2,910$	**d.** $25,811 \div 487$
Estimation:	Estimation:
Exact:	Exact:
Error of estimation:	Error of estimation:

5. Janet rides the bus to work, and the bus fare (one-way) is $1.35. Round the cents to the nearest whole ten and estimate the amount that she pays monthly to ride the bus to and from work if she works 22 days in a month.

6. Elisa bought 7 lb of apples for $1.19 per pound and 3 blocks of cheese for $11.45 a piece. Estimate the total cost.

The following problem is not an estimation problem. It is also longer and more involved than what you are used to solving. It will take more than five minutes to solve. But do not give up! Problems in real life are not necessarily solved in five minutes, either. You may use your calculator. (See the answer key for hints.)

7. The town library needs to reduce its operating costs. They want to try a plan where the salary of the five people working there is reduced by 1/10 and other costs are reduced by 2/10.

Currently, three of the people working there have a monthly salary of $1,552, and two of them have a monthly salary of $1,267. The other monthly operating costs are $8,490.

Find the total monthly savings in dollars, if the library adopts the plan.

Lessons in Problem Solving

You can draw a **flowchart** to help you find the logical way to solve a multi-step problem.

Write in the flowchart *what* you plan to solve in each step. You can also write down other notes you feel are important about that step.

Note 1: You don't have to use a flowchart. Its purpose is to help you organize your thoughts. By making it, you are essentially finding the solution path—which is the most important and more challenging part of problem solving. After that, all you have to do is the calculations, which is the easier, mechanical part.

Note 2: Finding the "path" to the solution can take some time, and perhaps you will find that you need to backtrack a step and find another way. This is normal. Even in real life, problems in all areas of life are solved with a process that includes several attempts, backtracking, and changing plans. Think of problem solving as a <u>process</u>—not as something you "have" to get right the first time.

Look at the examples below, and solve the problems. Use extra paper for calculations if needed.

---

1. A large carpet costs $55.50, and a small one costs 2/5 of that price.
   Luis bought two of the smaller carpets. What was his change from $50?

---

2. Angela has two kinds of plastic containers. The larger ones hold 0.75 liters, and the smaller ones hold 7/10 of that amount.

   Can Angela fit 5 liters of soup into four large and five small containers?

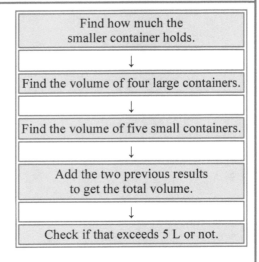

3. A 25-kg box of bolts was divided equally into 20 bags, and similarly,
   a 15-kg box of nuts was divided equally into 20 other bags.
   How much would one bag of bolts and one bag of nuts weigh together?

   Obviously you need to divide. Look at the <u>three</u> different ways to do the first division:

Way 1:	Way 2:	Way 3:
Divide 25,000 grams by 20. Your answer will be in grams.	Divide 25.000 kg by 20. Your answer will be a decimal and in kilograms.	Divide first by 10, and then the result by 2.

Here is a "flowchart" to illustrate the solution process.

Now you solve the problem.

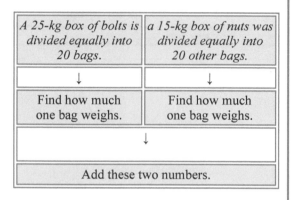

4. A company sells jars of jam in three different sizes. The largest size is 670 g,
   the medium size is 3/4 of that, and the smallest size is 2/3 of the medium size.

   a. Find the weight of the medium and smallest-sized jars.
   Round the weights to the nearest gram.

   b. Find the total weight of one large, one medium, and one small-sized jar.

5. John spent 4/9 of his money and Karen spent 4/7 of hers. Now they each have $30.60 left. How much more did Karen have initially than John?

You need to read this carefully and solve it in parts. To find out *how much more*, we need to know both numbers. So, first we need to find out how much Karen had and how much John had initially. Both of those can be solved separately using the bar model method.

The bar model below will help you solve how much money John had initially.

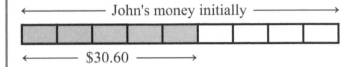

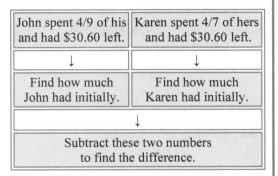

John spent 4/9 of his and had $30.60 left.	Karen spent 4/7 of hers and had $30.60 left.
↓	↓
Find how much John had initially.	Find how much Karen had initially.
↓	
Subtract these two numbers to find the difference.	

6. A company is taking 569 employees to a water park. It is 30 miles each way.
Each bus seats 43 people. The cost for each bus is $2.15 per mile.

    a. How many buses do they need?

    b. What are the transportation costs?

7. A washing machine has been discounted by 1/10 of its price, and now it costs $360.
Another washer has been discounted by 2/5 of its price, and now it costs $348.
Find the price difference between the two washers *before* the discount.
Hint: Draw two bar models, one for the price of each washer.

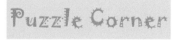 **a.** The decimal point key does not work in Henry's calculator.
But Henry discovered a way to enter decimals into his
calculator without using the decimal point key!

Find how he did it for these numbers: 0.1, 0.81, 0.492 and 3.55.

b. Find a way to calculate 1.38 × 0.39 with the calculator, without using the decimal point key.

Chapter 1 Mixed Review

In this mixed review lesson, we review some topics from 5th grade.

1. Are the following subtractions correct? If not, correct them.

a. Andy's calculation:

$4\frac{3}{8} - 1\frac{5}{8} = 3\frac{2}{8}$

b. Lillian's work

$$11\frac{2}{9}$$
$$-\ 4\frac{3}{9}$$
$$\overline{\quad 7\frac{8}{9}}$$

c. Jo's work: $3\frac{5}{12} - 2\frac{9}{12} = 3\frac{5}{12} - 2 - \frac{5}{12} - \frac{4}{12}$

$= 1 - \frac{4}{12} = \frac{8}{12} = \frac{2}{3}$

2. Write an addition sentence to match each illustration, and solve.

a.

b.

3. Measure the angles 1, 2, 3 and 4 of this polygon. Then label each angle as acute, right, or obtuse.

angle 1: _____° ; _____

angle 2: _____° ; _____

angle 3: _____° ; _____

angle 4: _____° ; _____

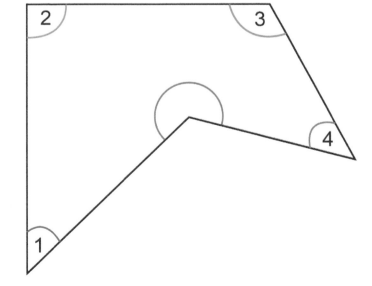

4. How can you find out the angle measure of the fifth angle? It is *a reflex angle –* it measures more than 180°.

5. Use the number lines below to put the given fractions in order.

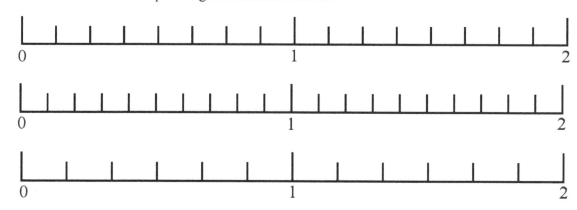

a. $\dfrac{5}{6}$, $\dfrac{8}{10}$, $\dfrac{7}{8}$, $\dfrac{9}{10}$, $\dfrac{7}{10}$

b. $\dfrac{9}{8}$, $\dfrac{11}{10}$, $\dfrac{7}{6}$, $\dfrac{12}{10}$, $\dfrac{10}{8}$

___ < ___ < ___ < ___ < ___   ___ < ___ < ___ < ___ < ___

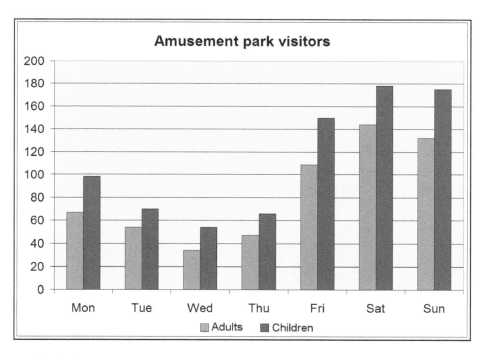

6. **a.** Which day was the busiest?

b. These numbers are visitors counts **for adults** for the days shown on the chart:

67 54 34 47 109 144 132

Find the daily average adult visitor count for this week, to the nearest whole number.

c. Estimate from the chart the child visitor counts for Friday, Saturday, and Sunday, the best you can. Then calculate their average, to the nearest whole number.

Chapter 1 Review

1. Divide and indicate the remainder, if any. Use long division.

   a. $6,764 \div 81$

   b. $309,855 \div 46$

2. How many times can you subtract 9 from 23,391 before you "hit" zero?

3. If you spend exactly $2.25 every day to make a phone call, how much will those phone calls cost you in a year?

4. If 5,000 people need to be moved from place A to place B by bus, and one bus seats 46 people, how many buses are needed?

5. An airplane travels at a constant speed of 880 km per hour. *Estimate* about how long it will take for it to fly 5,800 km.

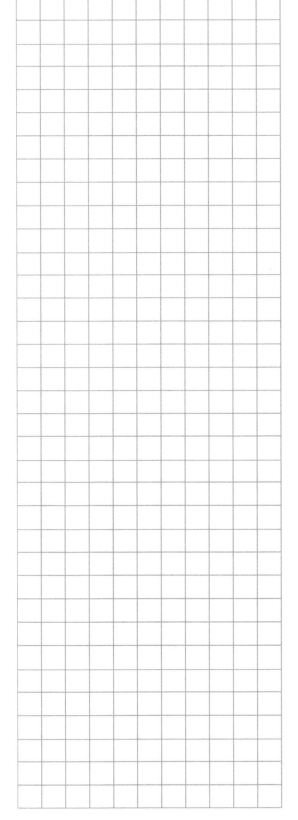

6. Three boxes of tea bags cost $15.90.
   How much do two boxes cost?

7. Write the expressions using an exponent. Then solve.

   a. $5 \times 5 \times 5 \times 5$ **d.** $100 \times 100 \times 100$

   b. $1 \times 1 \times 1 \times 1 \times 1 \times 1$ **e.** two to the sixth power

   c. 30 squared   **f.** three cubed

8. **a.** The perimeter of a square is 80 cm. What is its area?

   b. One edge of a cube measures 11 m. What is its volume?

9. Fill in.

   a. 25^3 gives us the _____ of a _____ with edges _____ units long.

   b. 3×9^2 gives us the _____ of _____ _____ with sides _____ units long.

10. Write in normal form (as a number).

   a. $2 \times 10^5 + 3 \times 10^2 + 9 \times 10^0$

   b. $2 \times 10^7 + 8 \times 10^6 + 3 \times 10^4 + 1 \times 10^3$

11. Write in order from the smallest to the largest.

a. 10^7 707,000 7,000,000	**b.** 4×10^5 5×10^4 450,000

12. Round to the place of the underlined digit. Be careful with the nines!

   a. $14\underline{9},601 \approx$ _____   **b.** $2,9\underline{9}9,307 \approx$ _____

   c. $59\underline{7},104,865 \approx$ _____   **d.** $559,9\underline{9}8,000 \approx$ _____

Chapter 2: Expressions and Equations
Introduction

In this chapter students start learning *algebra* – in a nutshell, the way to "do arithmetic with variables". Algebra enables us to solve real-life problems abstractly, in terms of variable(s) instead of numbers, and it is a very powerful tool.

Special notes for this chapter: algebra

The chapter focuses on two important basic concepts: **expressions** and **equations**. We also touch on inequalities and graphing on a very introductory level. In order to make the learning of these concepts easier, the expressions and equations in this chapter do not involve negative numbers (as they typically do when studied in pre-algebra and algebra). Integers are introduced in part 6-B, and then Math Mammoth grade 7 deals with algebraic concepts including with negative numbers.

We start out by reviewing the order of operations. Then the lessons focus on algebraic expressions. Students encounter the exact definition of an expression, a variable, and a formula, and practice writing expressions in many different ways. They study equivalent expressions and simplifying expressions. Length and area are two simple contexts I have used extensively for students to learn to write and simplify expressions.

In these lessons, students have opportunities to **write real-world scenarios in terms of variables**. In other words, they *decontextualise* – they abstract a given situation and represent it symbolically. Then, as they learn algebra, they learn to manipulate the representing symbols as if they have a life of their own, without necessarily attending to their referents, and to reason abstractly about those quantities represented by the variables.

The other major topic of the chapter is equations. Students learn some basics, such as, the solutions of an equation are the values of the variables that make the equation true. They use properties of operations and the idea of maintaining the equality of both sides of an equation to solve simple one-step equations. I have also included a few easy two-step equations.

Next, students solve and graph simple inequalities, again practicing the usage of variables to represent quantities. Lastly, they are introduced to the usage of *two* variables in algebra, including how to graph that relationship on a coordinate plane. This is an important topic, as so many real-life situations involve a relationship between two quantities, and graphing that relationship is an important tool in mathematical modeling.

You will find free videos covering many topics of this chapter of the curriculum at https://www.mathmammoth.com/videos/ (choose 6th grade).

The Lessons in Chapter 2

	page	span
The Order of Operations	45	*2 pages*
Expressions, Part 1	47	*2 pages*
Terminology for the Four Operations	49	*2 pages*
Words and Expressions	51	*2 pages*
Expressions, Part 2	53	*2 pages*
Writing and Simplifying Expressions 1: Length and Perimeter	55	*3 pages*
More on Writing and Simplifying Expressions	58	*3 pages*
Writing and Simplifying Expressions 2: Area	61	*5 pages*

Multiplying and Dividing in Parts 66   *4 pages*

The Distributive Property 70   *4 pages*

Equations 74   *4 pages*

Solving Equations 76   *4 pages*

Writing Equations 80   *2 pages*

Inequalities 82   *4 pages*

Using Two Variables 86   *4 pages*

Chapter 2 Mixed Review... 90   *2 pages*

Chapter 2 Review 92   *4 pages*

Helpful Resources on the Internet

We have compiled a list of Internet resources that match the topics in this chapter. This list of links includes web pages that offer:

- **online practice** for concepts;
- online **games**, or occasionally, printable games;
- **animations** and interactive **illustrations** of math concepts;
- **articles** that teach a math concept.

We heartily recommend you take a look at the list. Many of our customers love using these resources to supplement the bookwork. You can use the resources as you see fit for extra practice, to illustrate a concept better and even just for some fun. Enjoy!

https://l.mathmammoth.com/gr6ch2

SCAN ME

The Order of Operations

The Order of Operations (PEMDAS)

1) Solve what is within the **parentheses (P)**.

2) Solve **exponents (E)**.

3) Solve **multiplication (M)** and **division (D)** from left to right.

4) Solve **addition (A)** and **subtraction (S)** from left to right.

<u>Note</u>: From now on, we will use the raised dot · for the multiplication symbol. This is because we will be studying algebra, and × can be confused with the letter *x*, often used in algebra.

So, for example, we will write $5 \cdot 2$ to signify five times two.

Example 1. Solve $200 - (10 - 4 + 5)^2$.

1. Solve what is within the parentheses: $10 - 4 + 5$. Since subtractions and additions are on the same level, solve them from left to right: $10 - 4 + 5 = 11$. The expression is now $200 - 11^2$.

2. Next, solve the exponent: $11^2 = 121$. The expression is now $200 - 121$.

3. Lastly, subtract. $200 - 121 = 79$.

Example 2. $\dfrac{10 + 50}{12 - 6}$.

This expression is *not* the same as $10 + 50 \div 12 - 6$. Instead, the fraction line works as a grouping symbol, grouping together what is above and below the line, so that the division is to be done *last*. The expression is actually $(10 + 50) \div (12 - 6)$.

First, solve the expressions above and below the line (as if they were grouped using parentheses), and lastly divide:

$$\frac{10 + 50}{12 - 6} = \frac{60}{6} = 10$$

Example 3a. Here is an expression that has only *multiplications* and *divisions*: $20 \cdot 2 \div 4 \cdot 10$.

Those operations are on the SAME level in the order of operations, but that does *not* mean that multiplications are solved before divisions. Instead, they are solved in order from left to right.

$$20 \cdot 2 \div 4 \cdot 10$$
$$= \quad 40 \div 4 \cdot 10$$
$$= \quad\quad 10 \cdot 10 = 100$$

Example 3b. Let's rewrite the expression from 3a. using the fraction line for division—it will become easier!

Notice, there is a division by 4:

$$20 \cdot 2 \div 4 \cdot 10$$

This means that 4 needs to be in the denominator.

The expression can be written as $20 \cdot \dfrac{2}{4} \cdot 10$ or

as $\dfrac{20 \cdot 2}{4} \cdot 10$ (either is correct).

Comparing to the original expression $20 \cdot 4 \div 4 \cdot 10$, it looks quite different, but it is now easier to see what needs done. Verify that you get the same answer as in example 3a.

---

1. Put parentheses into the equations to make them true.

a. $100 - 50 - 50 = 100$ **b.** $200 \div 10 + 10 + 5 = 15$ **c.** $50 + 50 \cdot 4 - 10 = 390$

2. Rewrite each expression using the fraction line, then solve. Compare each expression in the top row of boxes to the one below it. *Hint: Only whatever comes right after the ÷ sign needs to be in the denominator.*

a. $64 \div 8 \cdot 4$	b. $64 \div (8 \cdot 4) \cdot 2$	c. $4 \cdot 8 \div 4 \cdot 2$
d. $64 \div (8 \cdot 4)$	e. $64 \div 8 \cdot 4 \cdot 2$	f. $(4 \cdot 8) \div (4 \cdot 2)$

3. Find the value of these expressions.

a. $150 + 2 \cdot 10$	b. $5^2 \cdot 2^3$	c. $3^2 \cdot (150 + 900) \div 3$
d. $\dfrac{12 + 9}{4 + 1}$	e. $\dfrac{5^2}{3^2}$	f. $\dfrac{2^3}{8} + 10^3$
g. $(6 + 6)^2 \cdot (15 - 5)^2$	h. $40 + 80 \div 2 \cdot 4 - 15$	i. $\dfrac{7^2}{7} \cdot 7$

4. Write the expressions in a shorter way, using multiplication. Find their values.

   a. $20\,000 - 500 - 500 - 500 - 500 - 500 - 500 - 500$

   b. $70 + 70 + 70 + 70 + 70 + 70 + 120 + 120 + 120 + 120 + 120$

5. Write the expressions in a shorter way, using exponents. Find their values.

   a. $2 \cdot 2 \cdot 2 \cdot 2 \cdot 2 \cdot 2 \cdot 2 + 5 \cdot 5 \cdot 5$

   b. $5 \cdot 100 \cdot 100 \cdot 100 - 2 \cdot 10 \cdot 10 \cdot 10 \cdot 10 \cdot 10$

Expressions, Part 1

Expressions in mathematics consist of: • numbers; • mathematical operations ($+$, $-$, $\cdot$, $\div$, exponents); • letters, such as x, y, a, T and so on. These letters signify numbers whose value might *vary*. They are called *variables*.	**Examples of expressions:** $5 + 6$ $\quad\dfrac{bh}{2}\quad$ $12 \cdot 9 - 7 \cdot 5$ $2^4 - x$ $\quad\dfrac{x+y}{2}\quad$ $T - 5$

Note 1. Expressions do *not* have an "equals" sign (=)! (It is *equations* that do.)

Note 2. In algebra, the multiplication sign $\cdot$ is omitted between two variables and between a number and a variable. So, bh means b times h, and $9t^2$ means 9 times t^2.

What do we do with expressions?

One main thing is that we can find the *value* of an expression by calculating it. This is also called *evaluating the expression*. For example, the value of $5 + 6$ is 11. The value of $12 \cdot 9 - 7 \cdot 5$ is 73.

If the expression contains a variable, such as $T - 5$, then we cannot find its value unless we know the value of the variable. For example, if T is 12, then the expression $T - 5$ has the value $12 - 5 = \underline{7}$.

Example 1. Evaluate the expression $x^4 - y$ when x has the value 2, and y has the value 7. Simply write "2" in place of x and "7" in place of y, and calculate: $$2^4 - 7 = 16 - 7 = \underline{9}$$	**Example 2.** Evaluate $24 - 6p$ when p has the value 3. Here, $6p$ signifies 6 times p. The multiplication sign is omitted between a number and a variable. We substitute 3 in place of p, and get: $$24 - 6 \cdot 3 = 24 - 18 = \underline{6}$$

1. Evaluate the expressions when the value of the variable is given.

a. $7z$ when $z = 3$	**b.** $5x^2$ when $x = 2$
c. $2x + 18$ when $x = 5$	**d.** $\dfrac{35}{z} \cdot 13$ when $z = 5$
e. mn^2 when $m = 5$ and $n = 3$	**f.** $\dfrac{3}{5}s$ when $s = 25$
g. $\dfrac{x^4}{x^2}$ when $x = 10$	**h.** $\dfrac{1}{9}y - 4$ when $y = 81$

2. Evaluate the expression $100 - x^2$ for the given values of the variable x.

Variable	Expression $100 - x^2$	Value
$x = 3$	$100 - 3^2$	91
$x = 4$		
$x = 5$		
$x = 6$		

3. Find the value of the expressions if $p = 14$ and $s = 5$.

a. $80 - p - s$	**b.** $80 - (p - s)$
c. $80 + p + s$	**d.** $80 - (p + s)$

4. **a.** Which of the expressions (3a), (3b), (3c) and (3d) had the same value?

   b. Check if those same expressions still have the same value if you use some other values for p and s.

   c. What do you think: do those expressions *always* have the same value, no matter what p and s are?
   If so, they are called **equivalent expressions**.

5. Write a single expression for each problem. (Make sure that you write an expression, not just the answer! We are practicing writing expressions with numbers only now, so that you will be able to write them with variables later on.)

   a. What is the total value, in cents, of five 10-cent coins, five 5-cent coins, two 20-cent coins and seven 50-cent coins?

   b. Margaret has 64 marbles. Tom has 15 less than Margaret. Henry has twice the amount of marbles Tom has. How many marbles does Henry have?

   c. What is the area of the colored part?

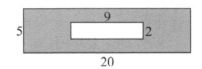

   d. What is the area of the colored part?

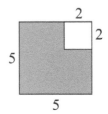

Terminology for the Four Operations

Study carefully the illustrations below to learn the terminology used with the four operations.

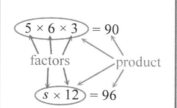

$(5 + 8 + 13) = 26$

addends   sum

$(x + 20) = 70$

$(55 - 17) = 38$

minuend   difference

subtrahend

$(x - 14) = 2$

The **m**inuend comes before the **s**ubtrahend, just like "M" comes before "S" in the alphabet.

$(5 \times 6 \times 3) = 90$

factors   product

$(s \times 12) = 96$

dividend   quotient

$\dfrac{x}{20} = 5$

divisor

Example 1. The sum of 5, 6 and z is written as $5 + 6 + z$.

Example 2. The expression $1 + 100 + 13$ is a sum, even though it has not been calculated yet. You can call it the *sum written*, and the answer 114 you can call the sum that has been *solved* or *calculated*.

Example 3. Similarly, the expression $55 - 40$ is a *difference*. Specifically, it is the difference between 55 and 40. The answer, 15, is also called the difference. You can differentiate between the two by saying that $55 - 40$ is the *difference written*, and the answer 15 is the difference *solved*.

Example 4. The difference between x and 15 is written as $x - 15$, *not* the other way around.

Example 5. The product of 5, x and y is written as $5 \cdot x \cdot y$ or as $5xy$. Normally, however, the multiplication symbol is simply <u>omitted</u> between letters (ax) or between a number and a letter ($5x$).

Example 6. The quotient of x and 4 is written as $\dfrac{x}{4}$ or as $x \div 4$. It is far more common (and recommendable) to use the fraction line and not the symbol $\div$ when we involve letters (variables).

Example 7. The quotient of 6 and y is written as $\dfrac{6}{y}$, not $\dfrac{y}{6}$.

1. Fill in the table, calculating the sum, difference, product and quotient of the numbers.

numbers	sum	difference	product	quotient
a. 50 and 2				
b. 5 and 3				

2. *Write* the sum, difference, product and quotient of the numbers and letters (you *cannot* calculate anything).

numbers/letters	sum	difference	product	quotient
a. x and 6				
b. z and w				

3. Match the expressions.

a. the product of 5 and T   5 − T   29   **e.** the difference between T and 5

b. the quotient of 5 and T   T − 5 $\dfrac{T}{5}$ **f.** the sum of T and 5

c. the product of 6 and 5   30   5T   **g.** the sum of 5, 15 and 9

d. the quotient of T and 5   5 ÷ T   T + 5   **h.** the difference between 5 and T

4. Write an equation, and find the part that is not given.

Statement	Equation
a. The quotient is 5, the divisor is 8, the dividend is _____.	_____ ÷ _____ = _____
b. The subtrahend is _____, the difference is 15 and the minuend is 45.	
c. The factors are 5, 6 and 8, and the product is _____.	
d. The addends are 7, 8 and _____, and the sum is 100.	

5. **a.** Write a multiplication problem, using three factors, where the product is 0.

  b. Write a division problem where the dividend is 120 and the quotient is less than 15.

  c. Using four addends, write a sum that is less than 9.

In these two problems, the *minuend* is unknown: To find it, use "addition backwards." This means you *add* the difference and the subtrahend.	_____ − 56 = 67 **Add:** 67 + 56 = 123. The missing number is <u>123.</u>	x − 400 = 1,200 **Add:** 1,200 + 400 = 1,600. Solution: x = <u>1,600.</u>

6. Find a strategy that always works for finding an unknown *subtrahend*. Use it to solve these problems.

a. 56 − _____ = 19

b. 4,203 − x = 553

7. Find a strategy that always works for finding an unknown *divisor*. Use it to solve these problems.

a. $\dfrac{56}{y} = 7$

b. $\dfrac{535}{x} = 5$

Words and Expressions

Words and expressions 1: addition		Words and expressions 2: multiplication	
"90 added to w"	$w + 90$	"15 multiplied by z"	$15z$
"the sum of 4, r and s"	$4 + r + s$	"the product of 2, x and y"	$2xy$
"17 more than a"	$a + 17$	"6 times a"	$6a$

Words and expressions 3: subtraction		Words and expressions 4: division	
Study these carefully. Students often get fooled with expressions relating to subtraction!		"3 over z squared"	$\dfrac{3}{z^2}$
"x subtracted from 7"	$7 - x$		
"5 less than 90"	$90 - 5$	"the quotient of y and 56"	$\dfrac{y}{56}$
"s less than 11"	$11 - s$		

1. Write an expression.

  a. the product of 7 and y **b.** 7 more than S

  c. the quotient of $5s$ and 8   **d.** 9 less than x

  e. r added to 190   **f.** 8 times d

  g. x less than 9   **h.** 14 subtracted from n

2. Write an expression for each scenario.

  a. The difference between s and 300, multiplied by 30.

  b. The sum of 35 and x divided by 7.

  c. The quotient of 200 and 40, subtracted from y.

3. Find the value of the expressions you wrote in exercise 2 when ...

  a. ... the variable s has the value 1,200.

  b. ... the variable x has the value 42.

  c. ... the variable y has the value 800.

Using the term "quantity"

How should you read the expression $\dfrac{t}{5+6}$?

If you read it as "t divided by 5 plus 6," it could be confused with $\dfrac{t}{5}+6$. The solution is to use the the word "quantity" or "sum" when referring to "5 + 6." It can be read in the following ways:

"t divided by the sum 5 plus 6"   "t divided by the sum of 5 and 6"

"t divided by the quantity 5 plus 6"   "the quotient of t and the quantity 5 plus 6" (not common)

Examples. Notice how we use the term "quantity" here.

$\dfrac{t}{5+6}$ "t divided by the quantity 5 + 6" *or* "t divided by the sum 5 + 6"

$2(x+1)$ "2 times the quantity $x + 1$" *or* "2 times the sum $x + 1$"

$(y-1)^2$ "the quantity $y - 1$, squared"

---

4. Write an expression.

   a. the quantity $2x - 1$ divided by 3   **b.** the quantity $5 + x$, cubed

   c. 5 times the quantity $x + 2$ **d.** 8 times the sum of 4, x and 2

   e. 2 times the quantity 10 minus s **f.** y divided by the quantity $y + 4$

   g. the quotient of the quantity $x + 4$ and x^2

5. Write an expression.

   a. 6 added to the product $7s$ **b.** the difference between $4s$ and 9

   c. Divide the sum 5 plus x by the difference between 5 and x.

   d. the difference between 6 and x, squared   **e.** the quantity 5 minus m, squared

   f. w^2 divided by the quantity $w - 1$ **g.** p^2 less than 100

   h. Subtract x from 7.   **i.** 100 more than x^2

---

a. The product of three numbers is 504. The numbers are consecutive. What are the numbers?

(Consecutive numbers are ones that follow each other, such as 10, 11 and 12.)

b. The sum of three consecutive numbers is 621. What are the numbers?

Expressions, Part 2

The volume of a cube can be calculated using the expression s^3, where s is the edge of the cube. We can also write this as a *formula*: $V = s^3$

A **formula** is an equation that explains how some quantities relate to each other. In this case, the formula $V = s^3$ shows how the volume of a cube relates to the length of its edge.

1. **a.** Find the volume of a cube with an edge $s = 4$ cm long.

   b. Find the volume of a cube with an edge $s = \frac{1}{2}$ m long.

2. The formula $F = C/5 \cdot 9 + 32$ allows you to calculate the temperature in Fahrenheit degrees (F) if you know the temperature in Celsius degrees (C). What is the temperature in Fahrenheit that corresponds to...

   a. 30°C?

   b. 18°C?

3. John uses the formula $C = mg/22$ to calculate how much it costs him in dollars to travel m miles, when the price of gas is g dollars per gallon (C is the cost). He gets 22 miles per gallon of gas. If gasoline costs \$3.25 per gallon, how much will it cost John to travel 380 miles?

4. Write an expression for each situation:

   a. The value, in cents, of p ten-cent coins (where p is a whole number).

   b. Father's salary is S dollars, and he pays 1/5 of it in taxes.
      Write an expression for the amount he pays in taxes.

   c. You bought m roses at \$4 each and n tulips at \$3.50 each.
      What was the total cost?

   d. The price of a serving of chicken and rice is p dollars
      and the price of a serving of shepherd's pie is q dollars.
      What is the total cost of buying both?

   e. You share the total cost of the two servings in part (d) equally with your friend.
      How much will each of you pay?

5. Can you find which of these expressions are equivalent? You can either reason logically or test them by checking the value of the expressions for several different values of the variable.

a.

$x + x$	$2x$	$x \cdot 2$	$x - x$

b.

$\dfrac{2x}{6}$	$\dfrac{x}{6}$	$\dfrac{x}{3}$	$\dfrac{x^2}{6}$

6. Write an expression. Solve.

   a. The sum of 3.2 and 5.3, multiplied by 2.

   b. First subtract 50 from 190, then divide the result by 5.

   c. Subtract from 100 the difference between 40 and 5.

   d. The quantity 2 times 5, cubed.

   e. 5 divided by 3 cubed.

   f. 2 times the quantity 10 minus 4, plus 3 times the quantity 5 plus 8.

   g. The difference between 61 and 30, divided by the quantity 5 squared.

   h. 7 less than 6 squared.

7. Find the value of the expressions, using the correct order of operations.

a. $20 + \dfrac{1 + 8 \cdot 10}{9}$	**b.** $60 - (1 + 2)^3$	**c.** $\dfrac{20 \cdot 30}{50 - 10} - 12$

8. Find a strategy that always works for finding an unknown *factor*. Use it to solve these problems.

a. _____ $\cdot\, 8 = 96$	**b.** $7m = 2{,}926$

Writing and Simplifying Expressions 1:
Length and Perimeter

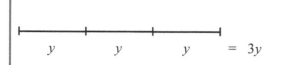

If the length of each line segment is y, then the total length of the line segments is $y + y + y$.

As you know, the shortcut for repeated addition is *multiplication*. So, we can *simplify* the sum $y + y + y$, and write **3y** in its place.

The expressions $y + y + y$ and $3y$ are **equivalent expressions**. This means that they have the same value no matter what value y has.

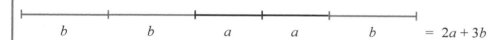

Here, we can write the total length as $b + b + a + a + b$, which is equivalent to $b + b + b + a + a$, which simplifies to $3b + 2a$. We can also write it as $2a + 3b$, because you can add in any order.

However, we *cannot* simplify the sum $2a + 3b$ any farther! The a and the b are not the same! Trying to add them would be like trying to add 2 meters and 3 liters. The expression is now as simple as it can get.

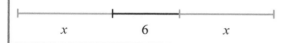

The total length here is $x + 6 + x$, which simplifies to $2x + 6$.

1. Write an expression for the total length of the line segments in simplified form.

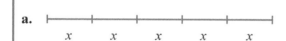

2. Write an expression for the perimeter of each shape in simplified form.

a.

x
4   4
x

b.

y
x x
y

c.

s s
s s
s s

d.

y
y y
y

e.

7
a
b

f.

t t
s s
3

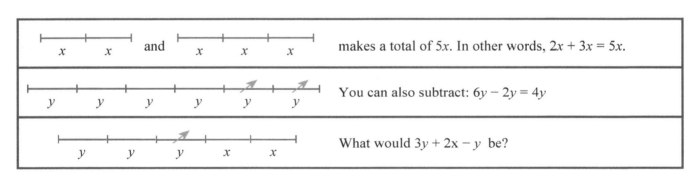

x x and x x x	makes a total of 5x. In other words, $2x + 3x = 5x$.
y y y y y y	You can also subtract: $6y - 2y = 4y$
y y y x x	What would $3y + 2x - y$ be?

3. Write an expression for the illustration, and simplify it.

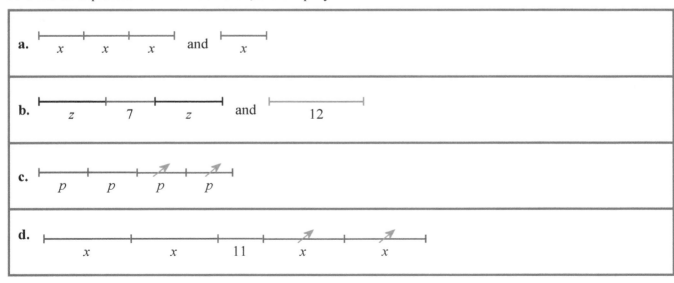

a. x x x and x

b. z 7 z and   12

c. p p p p

d. x x 11 x x

Example 1. The expression $3y + 2y + 8$ simplifies to $5y + 8$. You simply add the $3y$ and $2y$. You cannot add $5y$ and 8 though, so the expression is now as simple as it can get.

Example 2. The expression $8s - 3s$ can be simplified to $5s$.

Example 3. The expression $r + s + r + s + s - 3$ simplifies to $2r + 3s - 3$.

4. Simplify the expressions. Think of line segments to help you.

a. $c + c + c + c + c + 2$	**b.** $p + p + p + r + r$
c. $5 + x + x + 2 + x$	**d.** $z + z + x + 4 + x + z$
e. $m + m + q + m + s$	**f.** $8 + 1 + y + y + 4$
g. $5c + 2c$	**h.** $8p - 2p$
i. $6d - d$	**j.** $20x - 6x - 5x$
k. $5 + 2x + 3x - x$	**l.** $2a + 2 + 7a - 7x$

Some conventions

Recall, in algebra, we do <u>not</u> write multiplication signs between two variables, or between a number and a variable. For example, $8 \cdot a$ is written as $8a$, and $x \cdot y$ is written as xy.

We write the number *before* the variable(s), not vice versa. This means we write $6x$, not $x6$.

If several variables are multiplied, we write them in alphabetical order. So we write $2ad$, not $2da$.

Example 4. Simplify $5 \cdot x \cdot 6 \cdot x$.

Since we can multiply in any order, we can multiply $5 \cdot 6 = 30$. We can also write $x \cdot x$ in a shorter way as x^2. So the expression simplifies to $30x^2$.

Example 5. Simplify $5 + d \cdot 6 \cdot c$.

The term $d \cdot 6 \cdot c$ is written as $6cd$. We cannot add $6cd$ and 5, so the simplified expression is $6cd + 5$.

5. Simplify the expressions and remove the unnecessary multiplication signs.

a. $c \cdot c \cdot c$	**b.** $x \cdot x \cdot 4$
c. $5 \cdot x \cdot 6$	**d.** $2 \cdot z \cdot x$
e. $b \cdot 5 \cdot 9 \cdot a$	**f.** $y \cdot 4 + 8$
g. $c \cdot c + 2 \cdot 8$	**h.** $r \cdot 8 \cdot 4 - 2 \cdot 7$
i. $2 \cdot w \cdot 5 \cdot 4 \cdot x \cdot 7$	**j.** $p \cdot p \cdot 3 \cdot p$
k. $w \cdot w \cdot 10 \cdot 6 \cdot w \cdot w$	**l.** $r \cdot r - 3 \cdot 3$

More on Writing and Simplifying Expressions

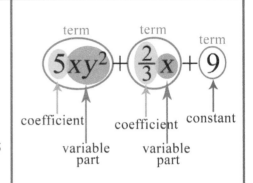

In mathematics, a **term** consists of numbers and/or variables that are *multiplied*. For example, $6x$ is a term and so is $0.9mn^2$.

A single number or a single variable is also a term. If the term is a single number, such as 4.5 or ¾, we call it a **constant**.

In the expression $5xy^2 + 4x + 9$, we have three terms, $5xy^2$, $4x$, and 9, that are separated by addition.

Is $s - 5$ a term? No, it is not since it contains subtraction. Instead, $s - 5$ is an expression consisting of two terms, s and 2, separated by subtraction.

term: coefficient, variable part; term: coefficient, variable part; term: constant

If a term is not a single number, then it has a **variable part** and a **coefficient**.

- The coefficient is a single number by which the variable or variables are multiplied.

- The variable part consists of the variables and their exponents.

For example, in $4.3ab$, 4.3 is the coefficient, and ab is the variable part.

<u>Note</u>: a term that consists of variables only still has a coefficient: it is one. For example, the coefficient of the term x^3 is one, because you can write x^3 as $1 \cdot x^3$.

1. Fill in the table.

Expression	the terms in it	coefficient(s)	Constants
$4a + 5b$	$4a$ and $5b$	4, 5	none
$300y$			
$11x + 5$			
$x + 12y + 9$			
$p \cdot 9$			
$8x^4y^3 + 10$			
$\dfrac{11}{26}p$			

2. Write an expression for each situation. Then list the terms and coefficients in it.

Expression in words	Expression	the terms in it	coefficient(s)
a. the value, in cents, of m five-cent coins			
b. the total cost of buying 20 apples that cost p each			
c. 15 less than v			

If two terms have the same variable part, they are called **like terms**. For example, $6a$ and $8a$ are like terms, and so are x^2 and $9x^2$, because their variable parts are identical.

Notice that $5x$ and 6 are *not* like terms. The first one has a variable part of x, and the other has no variable part.

To add or subtract like terms just add/subtract their coefficients. The variable part does not change.

Examples.	$7b + 8b + 2b = 17b$ (add $7 + 8 + 2 = 17$)	$r - t$ cannot be simplified, because the two terms are not like terms.
	$z^3 + 3z^3 = 4z^3$ (add $1 + 3 = 4$)	$5x - 2x + 6 = 3x + 6$ (subtract $5 - 2 = 3$)

3. Fill in the table.

Expression	Like terms, if any	Constants
$15x + 12z + 9z$	$12z$ and $9z$	none
$10 + 10y + 30y$		
$p \cdot 9 + 2$		
$8a - 2a + 10 + b + 7b$		
$8y + 7x + 6 + 15y - 2x$		

4. Simplify the expressions by adding and subtracting like terms.

a. $4x + 5x + 8$	**b.** $2z^2 + 11z^2$
c. $8m - 5m + 9n + 3n$	**d.** $8y + 7x + 6 + 15y - 2x$
e. $9m^2 - 2m^2 + 9 + 3m^2$	**f.** $16a + 15d + 10c - 2x - 7$
g. $17y + 2z + 9z - 6 - 5y$	**h.** $30h + 10h + 24 - w - 20 - 7h$

5. Find the value of the expressions if $x = 3$ and $y = 1/2$.

   a. $x + 2y$ **b.** $2(x + y)$

6. Find equivalent expressions. Don't be fooled!

a.	$s + s + s$	s^3	$3s$	$2s + s$

b.	$2y + 2x$	$x + y + x + b$	$y + y + x + x$	$yyxx$

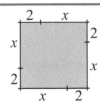

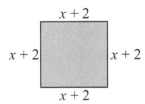

Each side of this square consists of line segments of lengths x and 2. We can write the expression $x + 2 + x + 2 + x + 2 + x + 2$ for the perimeter, and simplify it to $4x + 8$.

However, we can *also* think of each side as being the quantity $x + 2$, take that four times, and write the perimeter as the **product** $4(x + 2)$.

Obviously, the two expressions $4(x + 2)$ and $4x + 8$ are equivalent.

7. Write an expression for the perimeter in two ways.

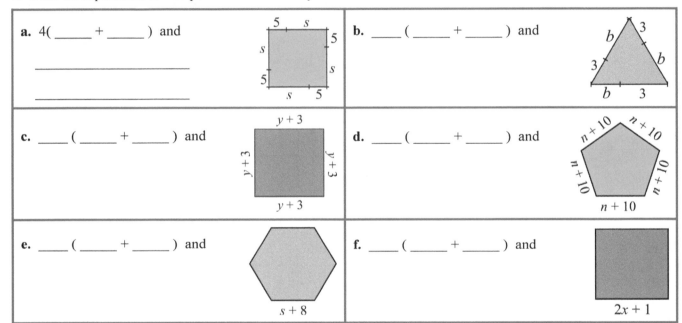

a. 4(_____ + _____) and

_____

_____

b. _____ (_____ + _____) and

c. _____ (_____ + _____) and

d. _____ (_____ + _____) and

e. _____ (_____ + _____) and

f. _____ (_____ + _____) and

8. Write an expression for each situation.

a. the perimeter of a square with sides of length $(a + 20)$

b. the cost of a book that originally cost p, but now is discounted by $5

c. the total cost of 5 headphones that originally cost p, but now are each discounted by $3

Puzzle Corner

a. The only variable you find in me is the most used variable in algebra. My constant term is the easiest fraction there is—kids learn it before first grade. The variable is multiplied by itself. I am a sum of two terms.

What am I?

b. My constant and my coefficients are whole numbers between 1 and 10. My constant is a prime and more than 5. I have three terms, separated by addition. My first term has one variable, and so does the second. The variables used are the two first letters of the alphabet. The two coefficients are distinct multiples of 2 that add up to 8.

What am I?

Writing and Simplifying Expressions 2: Area

![rectangle with sides l and w] w l	The two sides of this rectangle are l and w. Its area is then lw, because, as you know, we multiply the length and the width to find the area of a rectangle. (What is its perimeter?)
![square with side s] s s	In the case of a square, the expression for the area is $s \cdot s$. We can simplify it using an exponent: s^2.
![rectangle divided into little squares] x $3x$ $2x$	Here, each little square has a side of length x. The lengths of the sides of the whole rectangle are $2x$ and $3x$. We multiply them to get the area: $A = 3x \cdot 2x = 6 \cdot x \cdot x = 6x^2$. Notice also that each LITTLE square has an area of $xx = x^2$. There are six of these little squares, giving us, again, a total area of $6x^2$.

1. Write an expression for the *area* of the rectangle, and simplify it.

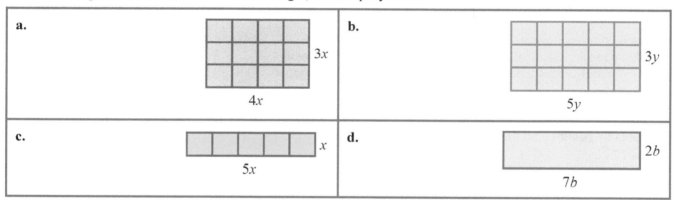

2. Write an expression for both the *area* and *perimeter* of each rectangle. Give them in simplified form.

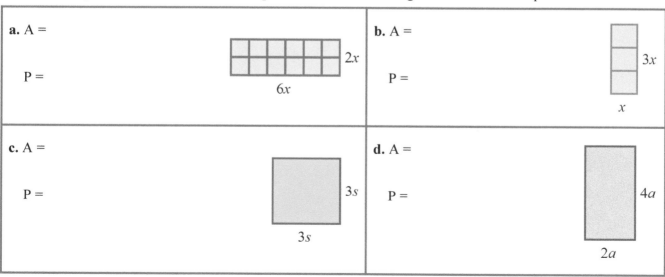

3. Write an expression for both the *area* and *perimeter* of each rectangle. Give them in simplified form.

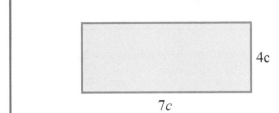

a. A =

P =

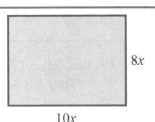

b. A =

P =

Here we have a shape that consists of two rectangles.

The area of the first rectangle is $4x \cdot 3x = 12x \cdot x = 12x^2$.

The area of the second rectangle is $5x \cdot 2x = 10x^2$.

To find the TOTAL area, add these two areas:

$A = 12x^2 + 10x^2 = \mathbf{22x^2}$

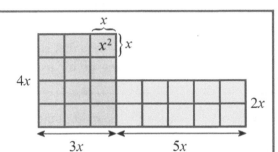

Notice that the expressions $12x^2$ and $10x^2$ are like terms—their variable parts are identical. Therefore, we can add the terms easily by just mentally adding their coefficients (the variable part stays the same).

Another reminder: each little square has sides of length x, and thus area x^2. So you could *also* find the total area by counting all the little squares: there are 22 little squares, each with an area of x^2, so the total area is $22x^2$.

To find the perimeter of this shape, first you need to figure out some of the missing lengths of the sides. Try to do that on your own! You should get $24x$ as the perimeter. Notice, the perimeter does NOT have x^2—we simply add many like terms that have x as their variable part, so the answer also has x as the variable part.

4. Write an expression for both the *area* and *perimeter* of each shape, in simplified form.

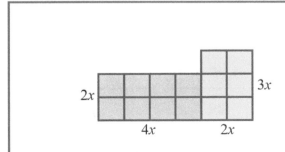

a. A =

P =

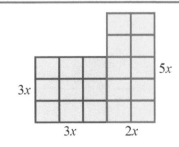

b. A =

P =

5. Write an expression, in simplified form, for both the *area* and *perimeter* of each shape.

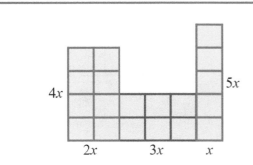

a. A =

P =

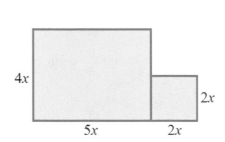

b. A =

P =

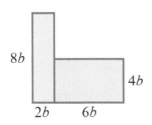

c. A =

P =

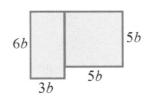

d. A =

P =

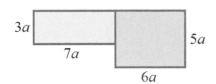

e. A =

P =

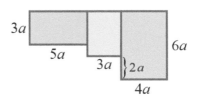

f. A =

P =

6. a. Write an expression for the area of this shape.

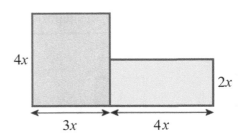

b. Evaluate the expression if $x = 5$ cm.

c. Evaluate the expression if $x = 10$ cm.

d. Is the area you get in (c) double the area you get in (b)?

7. a. You already wrote an expression for the area and perimeter of this shape in 5. e. Copy the expressions here so you can use them.

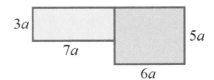

b. Evaluate the expression for the perimeter if the variable a has the value 2 centimeters.

c. Evaluate the expression for the perimeter if the variable a has the value 4 centimeters.

d. Is the perimeter you get in (c) double the perimeter you get in (b)?

e. Check if the same is true for area:

   - Find the area of the shape for two values of a: first 2 centimeters, then 4 centimeters.

   - Check if the area doubles, or if there is some other relationship between the two values for area.

8. Find the missing side length of the rectangles when one side and the area are given.

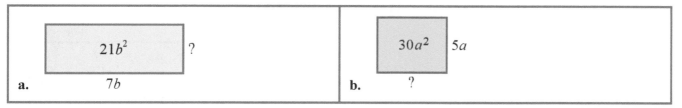

9. Find the missing side length when one side and the perimeter are given.

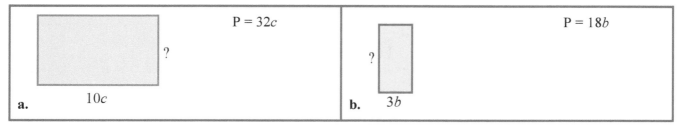

10. The area of a square is $4y^2$. What is the length of each side?

11. The perimeter of a rectangle is $42s$, and one of its sides is $13s$. How long is the other side?

12. Write an expression for each situation.

   a. What is the area of a square with sides of length $9r$?

   b. What is the perimeter of a regular pentagon with sides of length $8a$?

   c. Susan's age is S years. Her sister Ava is 3 years younger than Susan. Write an expression for Ava's age.

   d. A cheap pair of shoes costs p dollars. Another pair is $10 more expensive than the cheap pair. Write an expression for the cost of the more expensive pair.

   e. Write an expression for the cost of *five* pairs of the expensive shoes mentioned in (d).

Multiplying and Dividing in Parts

<table>
<tr>
<td>
You have already learned about **multiplying in parts** or **partial products**. For example, you can solve $7 \cdot 84$ by multiplying $7 \cdot 80$, then multiplying $7 \cdot 4$, and then adding the two results.

Essentially, we think of the second factor 84 as the **quantity** or **sum** $(80 + 4)$, and then multiply both of its parts separately by 7:
</td>
<td>

$7 \cdot 84$

$= 7 \cdot (80 + 4)$

$= 7 \cdot \boxed{80} + 7 \cdot \boxed{4}$

$= \quad 560 + \quad 28$

$= \quad 588$
</td>
</tr>
<tr>
<td>
We can use this idea with subtraction, also. Let's write 98 as the difference $(100 - 2)$. We can then multiply the product $8 \cdot 98$ thinking of it as $8 \cdot (100 - 2)$, and using partial products:
</td>
<td>

$8 \cdot (100 - 2)$

$= 8 \cdot 100 - 8 \cdot 2$

$= \quad 800 \quad - 16$

$= \quad 784$
</td>
</tr>
</table>

1. Write each given product using subtraction or addition. Then solve using partial products.

<table>
<tr>
<td>

a. $7 \cdot 99 = 7 \cdot (100 - 1)$

$= 700 - 7 = \underline{\hspace{2cm}}$
</td>
<td>

b. $4 \cdot 999 = 4 \cdot (\underline{\hspace{2cm}} - \underline{\hspace{1cm}})$

$=$
</td>
</tr>
<tr>
<td>

c. $5 \cdot 104 = 5 \cdot (\underline{\hspace{2cm}} + \underline{\hspace{1cm}})$

$=$
</td>
<td>

d. $5 \cdot 998$
</td>
</tr>
<tr>
<td>

e. $6 \cdot 98$
</td>
<td>

f. $7 \cdot 2{,}030$
</td>
</tr>
</table>

2. Write two expressions for the area of the whole rectangle, thinking of the large rectangle as the sum of two smaller ones. Study the example in part (a). In part (d), draw the picture yourself.

<table>
<tr>
<td>

a.

Total area: $\underline{3} \cdot (\underline{6} + \underline{4})$

The areas of the two rectangles:

$\underline{3} \cdot \underline{6}$ and $\underline{3} \cdot \underline{4}$
</td>
<td>

b.

Total area: $\underline{\hspace{1cm}} \cdot (\underline{\hspace{1cm}} + \underline{\hspace{1cm}})$

The areas of the two rectangles:

$\underline{\hspace{1cm}} \cdot \underline{\hspace{1cm}}$ and $\underline{\hspace{1cm}} \cdot \underline{\hspace{1cm}}$
</td>
</tr>
<tr>
<td>

c.

Total area: $\underline{\hspace{1cm}} \cdot (\underline{\hspace{1cm}} + \underline{\hspace{1cm}})$

The areas of the two rectangles:

$\underline{\hspace{1cm}} \cdot \underline{\hspace{1cm}}$ and $\underline{\hspace{1cm}} \cdot \underline{\hspace{1cm}}$
</td>
<td>

d.

Total area: $\underline{5} \cdot (\underline{2} + \underline{3})$

The areas of the two rectangles:

$\underline{5} \cdot \underline{2}$ and $\underline{\hspace{1cm}} \cdot \underline{\hspace{1cm}}$
</td>
</tr>
</table>

Remember **partial products** and the multiplication algorithm?

On the right, 25 · 39 is solved using partial products. The partial products are: 9 · 5, then 9 · 20, then 30 · 5, and lastly 30 · 20.

Notice there are *four* partial products. Notice also that we use 20 and 30 when we multiply, not 2 and 3. This is because the "2" in 25 really means 20, and the "3" in 39 really means 30.

```
        2 5
    ×   3 9
        4 5
    1   8 0
    1   5 0
  + 6   0 0
    9   7 5
```

3. **a.** Which partial products do 80 and 700 correspond to?

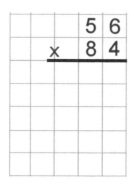

b. Solve using partial products.

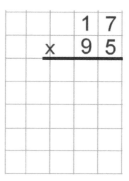

c. Solve using partial products.

17
× 95

Example 1. The picture illustrates the multiplication 38 · 57 using an area model. Study it carefully. It corresponds *exactly* to the partial products algorithm above: the total area is solved *in parts*. The total area of the rectangle is:

38 · 57 =   30 · 50 + 30 · 7

　　　　+ 8 · 50 + 8 · 7

　　　　= 1,500 + 210 + 400 + 56 = 2,166 **square units**

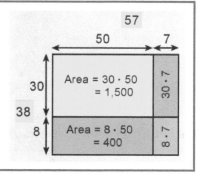

4. The rectangular area models illustrate two multiplications (not to scale). In each rectangular part, write how many square units its area is. Then, find the total area by adding the areas of the parts.

a. 29 · 17

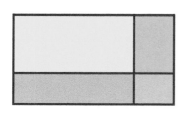

b. 75 · 36

We can also **divide a sum or difference in parts**.

Example 2. In the quotient $\dfrac{40 + 55}{5}$, we can divide $\dfrac{40}{5}$ and $\dfrac{55}{5}$ separately, and then add the results.

We get $\dfrac{40}{5} + \dfrac{55}{5} = 8 + 11 = 19$.

Example 3. Dividing in parts works equally well with subtraction: $\dfrac{120 - 48}{4} = \dfrac{120}{4} - \dfrac{48}{4} = 30 - 12 = 18$.

5. Divide in parts, then add or subtract the results.

a. $\dfrac{80 + 12}{2}$	b. $\dfrac{350 + 15}{5}$	c. $\dfrac{400 - 12}{4}$
d. $\dfrac{9{,}300 - 60}{3}$	e. $\dfrac{350 + 21 - 7}{7}$	f. $\dfrac{900 - 18}{9}$
g. $\dfrac{22 \text{ m } 9 \text{ cm}}{2}$	h. $\dfrac{40 \text{ kg } 750 \text{ g}}{5}$	i. $\dfrac{12 \text{ L } 600 \text{ ml}}{4}$

How can you make sense of this? Let's say you have both apples and oranges in a bag, and you are going to share them equally between 5 people. How many pieces of fruit will each person get? You could just mix all the pieces of fruit and divide the total number by five to find the answer, but you can also take only the apples and divide those by 5, and then take only the oranges and divide them by five. In essence:

$$\frac{\text{apples} + \text{oranges}}{5} = \frac{\text{apples}}{5} + \frac{\text{oranges}}{5}$$

(Of course, you probably want to divide the fruit separately in this situation, and not mix them. But the NUMBER of pieces of fruit that each person would get can be found either way.)

6. Divide in parts in your head. First, think how the dividend can be written in two or more parts.

a. $\dfrac{412}{2}$	b. $\dfrac{609}{3}$	c. $\dfrac{824}{8}$	d. $\dfrac{1{,}206}{6}$	e. $\dfrac{4{,}518}{9}$

7. You have 2 liters 250 milliliters of ice cream that you want to share equally with three of your friends (four people in total) at a birthday party. How much ice cream will each person get?
   Round your answer to the nearest 10 milliliters.

Dividing $\dfrac{21+2}{7}$ in parts, we get $\dfrac{21}{7}$ and $\dfrac{2}{7}$. While 21/7 is just 3, the other part, 2/7, has to be left as a fraction. We get $3 + \dfrac{2}{7} = 3\dfrac{2}{7}$. Of course, this is the same as writing the fraction $\dfrac{23}{7}$ as a mixed number.

8. Divide in parts. You will have a fraction in the answer.

a. $\dfrac{15+4}{5}$	**b.** $\dfrac{44+7}{11}$	**c.** $\dfrac{6+70}{7}$
d. $\dfrac{420+2}{6}$	**e.** $\dfrac{240+12+3}{4}$	**f.** $\dfrac{2+36+270}{9}$

9. Divide in parts in your head. First, think how the dividend can be written in two or more parts. See the example.

a. $\dfrac{403}{4} = \dfrac{400+3}{4} =$	**b.** $\dfrac{911}{3}$
c. $\dfrac{5{,}024}{5}$	**d.** $\dfrac{81}{4}$
e. $\dfrac{127}{3}$	**f.** $\dfrac{365}{6}$

Reminder: you can *only* divide in parts when there is a single number in the denominator (the divisor). In the expression $\dfrac{30+120}{3+7}$, we need to first solve 3 + 7. After that, you could divide in parts.

You could also simply calculate the two sums first to get 150/10 = 15.

10. Simplify. In some of these problems, it helps to divide in parts. Can you find which ones?

a. $\dfrac{3+4}{5+9}$	**b.** $\dfrac{12-5}{3+13+5}$
c. $\dfrac{30+50}{2+9}$	**d.** $\dfrac{6+24+240}{8}$
e. $\dfrac{120-3}{7-3}$	**f.** $\dfrac{100}{80-50}$

Fill in the blanks so the equations are true.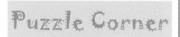

a. $\dfrac{\boxed{} - \boxed{}}{10} = 25 - \dfrac{3}{10}$ **b.** $\dfrac{\boxed{} - 3}{5} = 2\dfrac{1}{5} - \dfrac{\boxed{}}{\boxed{}}$

The Distributive Property

The **distributive property** states that $a(b + c) = ab + ac$

It may look like a meaningless or difficult equation to you now, but don't worry, it will become clearer!

The equation $a(b + c) = ab + ac$ means that you can *distribute* the multiplication (by a) over the sum $b + c$ so that you multiply the numbers b and c separately by a, and add last.

You have already used the distributive property! When you separated $3 \cdot 84$ into $3 \cdot (80 + 4)$, you then multiplied 80 and 4 *separately* by 3, and added last: $3 \cdot 80 + 3 \cdot 4 = 240 + 12 = 252$. We called this using "partial products" or "multiplying in parts."

Example 1. Using the distributive property, we can write the product $2(x + 1)$ as $2x + 2 \cdot 1$, which simplifies to $2x + 2$.

Notice what happens: Each term in the sum $(x + 1)$ gets multiplied by the factor 2! Graphically:

$$2(x + 1) = \underline{2x} + \underline{2 \cdot 1}$$

Example 2. To multiply $s \cdot (3 + t)$ using the distributive property, we need to multiply *both* 3 and t by s:

$$s \cdot (3 + t) = s \cdot 3 + s \cdot t, \text{ which simplifies to } 3s + st.$$

1. Multiply using the distributive property.

a. $3(90 + 5) = 3 \cdot \underline{} + 3 \cdot \underline{} =$	**b.** $7(50 + 6) = 7 \cdot \underline{} + 7 \cdot \underline{} =$
c. $4(a + b) = 4 \cdot \underline{} + 4 \cdot \underline{} =$	**d.** $2(x + 6) = 2 \cdot \underline{} + 2 \cdot \underline{} =$
e. $7(y + 3) =$	**f.** $10(s + 4) =$
g. $s(6 + x) =$	**h.** $x(y + 3) =$
i. $8(5 + b) =$	**j.** $9(5 + c) =$

Example 3. We can use the distributive property also when the sum has three or more terms. Simply multiply *each term* in the sum by the factor in front of the parentheses:

$$5(x + y + 6) = 5 \cdot x + 5 \cdot y + 5 \cdot 6, \text{ which simplifies to } 5x + 5y + 30$$

2. Multiply using the distributive property.

a. $3(a + b + 5) =$	**b.** $8(5 + y + r) =$
c. $4(s + 5 + 8) =$	**d.** $3(10 + c + d + 2) =$

Example 4. Now one of the terms in the sum has a coefficient (the 2 in $2x$):

$$6(2x + 3) = 6 \cdot 2x + 6 \cdot 3 = 12x + 18$$

3. Multiply using the distributive property.

a. $2(3x + 5) =$	**b.** $7(7a + 6) =$
c. $5(4a + 8b) =$	**d.** $2(4x + 3y) =$
e. $3(9 + 10z) =$	**f.** $6(3x + 4 + 2y) =$
g. $11(2c + 7a) =$	**h.** $8(5 + 2a + 3b) =$

To understand even better why the the distributive property works, let's look at an area model (this, too, you have seen before!).

The area of the whole rectangle is 5 times $(b + 12)$.

But if we think of it as *two* rectangles, the area of the first rectangle is $5b$, and of the second, $5 \cdot 12$.

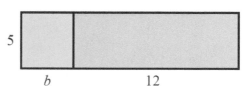

Of course, these two expressions have to be equal:

$$5 \cdot (b + 12) = 5b + 5 \cdot 12 = 5b + 60$$

4. Write an expression for the area in two ways, thinking of one rectangle or two.

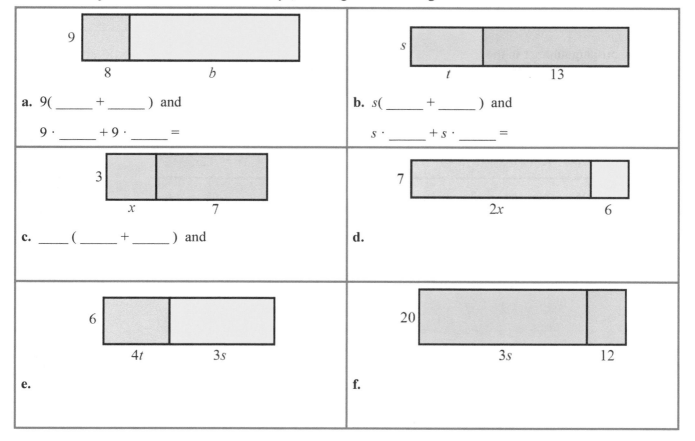

a. 9(_____ + _____) and

9 · _____ + 9 · _____ =

b. s(_____ + _____) and

s · _____ + s · _____ =

c. ____ (_____ + _____) and

d.

e.

f.

5. Find the missing number or variable in these area models.

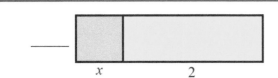

a. _____ $(x + 2) = 3x + 6$

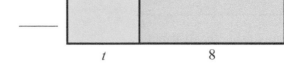

b. _____ $(t + 8) = 7t + 56$

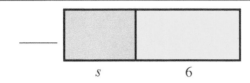

c. The total area is $9s + 54$.

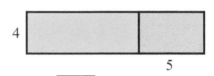

d. $4(\_\_\_\_ + 5) = 4z + 20$

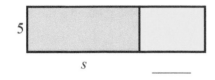

e. $5(s + \_\_\_\_) = 5s + 30$

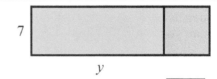

f. The total area is $7y + 42$.

6. Find the missing number in the equations.

a. _____ $(x + 5) = 6x + 30$	**b.** $10(y + \_\_\_\_) = 10y + 30$
c. $6(\_\_\_\_ + z) = 12 + 6z$	**d.** $8(r + \_\_\_\_) = 8r + 24$

7. Find the missing number in the equations. These are just a little bit trickier!

a. _____ $(2x + 5) = 6x + 15$	**b.** _____ $(3w + 5) = 21w + 35$
c. _____ $(6y + 4) = 12y + 8$	**d.** _____ $(10s + 3) = 50s + 15$
e. $2(\_\_\_\_ + 9) = 4x + 18$	**f.** $4(\_\_\_\_ + 3) = 12x + 12$
g. $5(\_\_\_\_ + 3) = 20y + 15$	**h.** $8(\_\_\_\_ + \_\_\_\_ + 7) = 40t + 8s + 56$

8. Write an expression for the perimeter of this regular heptagon as a *product*.
   Then multiply the expression using the distributive property

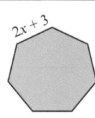

9. The perimeter of a regular pentagon is $15x + 5$. How long is one of its sides?

72

When we use the distributive property "backwards," and write a sum as a product, it is called **factoring**.
Example 5. The sum $5x + 5$ can be written as $5(x + 1)$. We took the SUM $5x + 5$ and wrote it as a PRODUCT— something times something, in this case 5 times the quantity $(x + 1)$.
Example 6. The sum $24x + 16$ can be written as the product $8(3x + 2)$.   *Notice* that the numbers 24 and 16 are *both divisible by 8*! That is why we write 8 as one of the factors.

10. Think of the distributive property "backwards," and factor these sums. Think of divisibility!

a. $6x + 6 =$ _____ $(x + 1)$	**b.** $8y + 16 = 8($ _____ $+$ _____ $)$
c. $15x + 45 =$ _____ $(x +$ _____ $)$	**d.** $4w + 40 =$ _____ $(w +$ _____ $)$
e. $6x + 30 =$ _____ $($ _____ $+$ _____ $)$	**f.** $8x + 16y + 48 =$ _____ $($ _____ $+$ _____ $+$ _____ $)$

11. Factor these sums (writing them as products). Think of divisibility!

a. $8x + 4 =$ _____ $(2x +$ _____ $)$	**b.** $15x + 10 =$ _____ $(3x +$ _____ $)$
c. $24y + 8 =$ _____ $($ _____ $+$ _____ $)$	**d.** $6x + 3 =$ _____ $($ _____ $+$ _____ $)$
e. $42y + 14 =$ _____ $($ _____ $+$ _____ $)$	**f.** $32x + 24 =$ _____ $($ _____ $+$ _____ $)$
g. $27y + 9 =$ _____ $($ _____ $+$ _____ $)$	**h.** $55x + 22 =$ _____ $($ _____ $+$ _____ $)$
i. $36y + 12 =$ _____ $($ _____ $+$ _____ $)$	**j.** $36x + 9z + 27 =$ _____ $($ _____ $+$ _____ $+$ _____ $)$

12. The perimeter of a square is $48x + 16$. How long is its side?

As a shopkeeper, you need to purchase 1,000 items to get a wholesale (cheaper) price of $8 per item, so you do. You figure you might sell 600 of them. You also want to advertise a $3 discount to your customers. What should the non-discounted selling price be for you to actually earn a $500 profit from the sale of these items?

Puzzle Corner

Epilogue: It may be hard to see now where distributive property or factoring might be useful, but it IS extremely necessary later in algebra when solving equations.

To solve the problem above, you *can* figure it out without algebra, but it becomes fairly straightforward if we write an equation for it. Let p be the non-discounted price. Then $p - \$3$ is the price with the discount. We get:

$$\text{What we need to take in} = \text{pay to supplier} + \text{profit}$$

$$600(p - \$3) = 1{,}000 \cdot \$8 + \$500$$

To solve this equation, one needs to use the distributive property in the very first step:

$$600p - \$1{,}800 = \$8{,}500$$

$$600p = \$10{,}300 \qquad \text{(Can you solve this last step yourself?)}$$

Equations

An **equation** has two expressions, separated by an equal sign: (expression) = (expression)	**These all are equations:**

An **equation** has two expressions, separated by an equal sign:

(expression) = (expression)

These all are equations:

$2(a + 6) = y$ $\qquad$ $0 = 0$

$9 = 8 + 8$ $\qquad$ $\dfrac{x + y}{2} = 5$

(a false equation)

$5 - x^2 = 2x + 7$

Some equations are *true*, and others are *false*.

$10 = 9$ is a false equation. $6 + 6 = 12$ is a true equation.

Some equations are neither. The equation $x + 1 = 7$ is neither true nor false. However, if x has a specific value, then we can tell if the equation is true or false. Is it true if x has the value 9?

What do we do with equations?

If the equation has a variable (or several) in it, we can try to *solve* the equation to find the values of the variable(s) that make the equation true.

For example, we can solve the equation $6 + x = 60$ for the unknown x. The value 54 makes the equation true: $6 + 54 = 60$. We say $x = 54$ is the **solution** or the **root** of the equation.

1. Label each as an equation or an expression.

   a. $2x - 3 = 8 + x$ $\qquad$ **b.** $y^2 - 9$ $\qquad$ **c.** $4 + 2 = 6$ $\qquad$ **d.** $\dfrac{1}{2}x^4 - 5$ $\qquad$ **e.** $\dfrac{T + 2D}{C}$

2. Write the statements as equations. Use a letter for the unknown (the "secret number" or "a number"). Then solve the equations.

   a. When you add 4 and a secret number, you get 10.

   Equation: _____ $4 + x = 10$ _____ $\qquad$ Solution: ___ $x = 6$ ___

   b. When a secret number is subtracted from 100, the difference is 35.

   Equation: _____ $\qquad$ Solution: _____

   c. The product of 3 and a number is 63.

   Equation: _____ $\qquad$ Solution: _____

   d. When you divide a number by 7, the result is 12.

   Equation: _____ $\qquad$ Solution: _____

   e. 19 less than a certain number gives us 394.

   Equation: _____ $\qquad$ Solution: _____

   f. The quotient of 60 and a secret number is equal to 12.

   Equation: _____ $\qquad$ Solution: _____

Solving the equation means finding the value(s) of the variable(s) that make the equation TRUE. The solutions of the equation are also called **roots**.

Example 1. Find the root (solution) of the equation $x^2 + 15 = 64$ in the set $\{2, 5, 7, 15\}$.

Try each number from the set in the equation, substituting x with that number, and check if it fulfills the equation (makes it true):

$2^2 + 15 \neq 64$ $7^2 + 15 = 64$ (The symbol $\neq$ is read as "not equal".)

$5^2 + 15 \neq 64$ $15^2 + 15 \neq 64$ So, 7 is the only root to the equation in the given set.

3. **a.** Is $x = 7$ a root for the equation $x^2 - 17 = 33$?

   b. Is $a = 78$ a root for the equation $a/3 = 26$?

4. **a.** Find the roots of the equation $x^2 + 18 - 9x = 0$ in the set $\{1, 2, 3, 10, 7, 6\}$.

   b. Find the root of the equation $3x - 5 = 2x$ in the set $\{2, 3, 4, 5, 6\}$.

5. Find a value for variable k that makes the equation $6k + 8 = 44$ false.

6. Which of the numbers 0, 1, 2 or 3 make the equation $\dfrac{y + 6}{y + 2} = 2$ true?

7. Write two different equations with the root $x = 11$.

8. Find the solution of the equation $\dfrac{y}{4} + 44 = 3y$ in the set of positive even numbers that are less than 20.

9. Matthew was studying the discounted prices of the items in his store. He denoted the original price as p, and used the expression $(4/5)p$, which is four-fifths of p, for the price after 1/5 discount.

   a. Calculate the discounted prices for items costing $1, $2, $5, $10 and $45.

   b. (Challenge) Find the original price for the last item. Guess and check!

Item	p	$(4/5)p$
Eraser	$1	
Pen	$2	
Tea	$5	
Bread	$10	
Backpack	$45	
Boots		$32

Solving Equations

Solving equations is like a "game." The "goal" of the game is to leave the unknown (such as x) **alone** on one side of the equation, or **isolate** it, so that we have $x =$ (something) or (something) $= x$.

The allowed "moves" in the game are these:
- You can *add* the same number to both sides of the equation;
- You can *subtract* the same number from both sides of the equation;
- You can *multiply* both sides of the equation by the same number;
- You can *divide* both sides of the equation by the same number.

Think of the balance: if you **add** the same thing to **both** pans of the balance, both sides will still weigh the same (though more than before)! Or, if you **take away** the same thing from **both** pans of the balance, both sides will STILL weigh the same (though less than before)!

Example 1. When we remove 6 from both sides of the pan balance below, the balance WILL stay balanced! The equation $3x + 6 = 36$ will "lose" 6 from both sides, and become $3x = 30$.

$$3x + 6 = 36 \qquad\qquad 3x = 30$$

Whatever you do (add, subtract, multiply, divide) to one side of the equation, you do to the other side as well. That preserves the equality of the two sides!

Study these examples carefully. They not only show how these simple equations are solved, but also illustrate *how to write down* the solution process—in two different ways. It is something you need to learn.

Example 2. The left side has the sum of x and 19. To make x appear alone, we *subtract 19 from both sides*. Notice how this is written in the solution. Now, on the left side, $+ 19 - 19$ equals zero, so, we have only x left. On the right side, we simply calculate $454 - 19 = 435$.

$$
\begin{aligned}
x + 19 &= 454 \\
-19 \quad &\quad -19 \\
\hline
x &= 435
\end{aligned}
$$

Lastly, we need to **check** our solution. To do that, write the solution 435 in place of x in the *original* equation, and check that it is a true equation: **Is 435 + 19 really 454?** Yes, it is.

Example 3. This time, 76 is subtracted from x, so *add* 76 to both sides. Here is another way to mark what is going to be done to both sides of the equation: write it in the right margin.

$$
\begin{aligned}
x - 76 &= 180 \qquad &|\, + 76 \\
x - 76 + 76 &= 180 + 76 \\
x &= 256
\end{aligned}
$$

On the left side, $- 76$ and $+ 76$ cancel each other (equaling zero). On the right side, we calculate $180 + 76$. We get 256.

Check: Does $256 - 76$ really equal 180? Yes, it does.

Example 4. To leave y alone on the left side, we **add** 72 to both sides.

$$
\begin{aligned}
y - 72 &= 489 \\
+72 \quad &\quad +72 \\
\hline
y &= 561
\end{aligned}
$$

Check: Is $561 - 72$ really 489? Yes, it is.

Example 5. To "undo" $48 + w$, we subtract 48 from both sides.

$$
\begin{aligned}
48 + w &= 91 \qquad &|\, - 48 \\
48 + w - 48 &= 91 - 48 \\
w &= 43
\end{aligned}
$$

Check: Is $48 + 43$ really 91? Yes, it is.

1. Solve these one-step equations. Look at the examples on the previous page, and write the steps to the solution. You can choose which way you will write them down (under the equation or in the margin).

a. $\quad 54 + x \;=\; 990$ $=$ $=$	**b.** $\quad x + 5.6 \;=\; 12.9$ $=$ $=$
c. $\quad x - 120 \;=\; 137$ $=$ $=$	**d.** $\quad w - 98 \;=\; 89$ $=$ $=$
e. $\quad 156 + s \;=\; 1{,}082$ $=$ $=$	**f.** $\quad t + 77 \;=\; 208$ $=$ $=$

Example 6. Here we will first simplify what is on the right side of the equation.

Simplify $45 + 18$.	$35 + x = 45 + 18$
Subtract 35 from both sides.	$35 + x = 63 \qquad \big| -35$
35 and -35 cancel each other. (This step could be omitted.)	$35 + x - 35 = 63 - 35$
The final result.	$x = 28$

Check: Is $35 + 28$ really equal to $45 + 18$? Yes, it is. So, the solution $x = 28$ is correct.

Example 7. You can always switch the two sides of an equation. This is especially handy if the unknown is on the right side at first.

$$460 = x + 98$$
$$x + 98 = 460 \qquad \big| -98$$
$$x = 362$$

Do you have to do this? No, you don't, but it can be quite helpful at times.

2. Solve.

a. $\quad y - 26 \;=\; 36 + 9$ $=$	**b.** $\quad z - 220 \;=\; 3 \cdot 100$ $=$	**c.** $\quad 200 + x \;=\; 430 + 80$ $=$
d. $\quad 2.4 + 9.1 \;=\; 7 + z$ $=$	**e.** $\quad 4 \cdot 7 + 30 \;=\; s - 86$ $=$	**f.** $\quad 8 + x + 2.5 \;=\; 20 - 8.2$ $=$

$8x = 120$	**Example 8.** Here, x is multiplied by 8. To "undo", divide both sides by 8.
$\dfrac{8x}{8} = \dfrac{120}{8}$	On the left side, the 8 in the denominator cancels the 8 in the numerator. On the right side, calculate $120 \div 8$.
$x = 15$	We get 15 as the root. Lastly, check: is $8 \cdot 15$ really 120?

Example 9. Here, x is divided by 9. To "undo" that and leave x by itself, multiply both sides by 9.

On the left, the 9s in the numerator and in the denominator cancel each other. On the right, calculate $54 \cdot 9$.

This is the final answer. To check, divide that by 9. Do you get 54?

$$\dfrac{x}{9} = 54 \quad \Big| \cdot 9$$

$$\dfrac{x}{9} \cdot 9 = 54 \cdot 9$$

$$x = 486$$

3. Solve these one-step equations. Write the solution steps in a manner similar to the examples above.

a. $\quad 5x = 350$	**b.** $\quad 10x = 17$	**c.** $\quad 7a = 2.8$
$=$	$=$	$=$
$=$	$=$	$=$
d. $\quad \dfrac{x}{51} = 4$	**e.** $\quad \dfrac{x}{9} = 60$	**f.** $\quad \dfrac{x}{100} = 1.2$
$=$	$=$	$=$
$=$	$=$	$=$

4. Solve. In these, the unknown may be on the right side, and/or you may need to first simplify something.

a. $\quad y \div 400 = 6 + 2$	**b.** $\quad 6 \cdot 9 = \dfrac{x}{20}$	**c.** $\quad 8x = 501 + 59$
$=$	$=$	$=$
$=$	$=$	$=$
$=$	$=$	$=$

5. **a.** Solve the equation $x = 2x$ in the set $\{5, 10, 15, 20\}$.

b. Can you find a solution to the equation outside of that set?
Hint: try some easy numbers.

6. Solve these equations. Think of equivalent fractions!

a. $\dfrac{x}{18} = \dfrac{5}{6}$	**b.** $\dfrac{14}{24} = \dfrac{7}{y}$	**c.** $\dfrac{5}{8} = \dfrac{z}{56}$

Example 10. This equation has several like terms ($3x$ and $4x$). But to isolate x, we need to have a single term with x, not several.

So, first we simplify $3x + 4x$ on the left side.

Now we divide both sides by 7.

Here is the final solution.

$$3x + 4x = 35$$
$$7x = 35 \mid \div 7$$
$$x = 5$$

Check: is $3 \cdot 5 + 4 \cdot 5$ equal to 35? Yes, it is, so the solution checks.

7. Solve these equations.

a. $\quad 2y + 5y = 49$ $=$	**b.** $\quad 10x - 8x = 42$ $=$	**c.** $\quad 7a + 2a - 5a = 52$ $=$
d. $\quad 2x + 3x = 29 - 14$ $=$	**e.** $\quad 7c - c = 3 \cdot 80$ $=$	**f.** $\quad 14x - 6x + 2x = 5 \cdot 40$ $=$

Two-step equations (*optional*). Remember, the goal in solving equations is to have the term with x by itself on one side of the equation. Study the examples of equations that are solved in two steps.	**Example 11.** $4x + 17 = 81 \mid -17$ $4x = 64 \mid \div 4$ $x = 16$	**Example 12.** $7x - 11 = 45 \mid +11$ $7x = 56 \mid \div 7$ $x = 8$

8. Solve the equations.

a. $\quad 2x + 5 = 27$ $=$	**b.** $\quad 3x - 8 = 34$ $=$	**c.** $\quad 7x + 5 = 54$ $=$
d. $\quad 10z - 7 = 97$ $=$	**e.** $\quad 832 = 3x + 85$ $=$	**f.** $\quad 56 + 21 = 5x - 3$ $=$

Writing Equations

Example. The perimeter of a square is 486 m. How long is its side?

This is an easy problem, but let's use it to learn to write equations! To write an equation for this problem, we need to first find what "thing" is unknown, and choose a variable for it.

The unknown is the length of the side. Let's choose s to represent that.

The equation needs to match this sentence: "The perimeter of a square is 486." The word "is" actually corresponds to the equals sign in our equation! So we just need to write an expression that uses our variable s for "the perimeter of a square."

That is easy: Since the perimeter of a square with side s is $4s$ (why?), the equation we want is $4s = 486$.

1. Write an equation for each situation (even if you could easily solve the problem without an equation). Then solve the equation.

   a. The value of a certain number of five-cent coins is 485 cents. How many five-cent coins are there?

   Hint: First choose a variable to represent the number of five-cent coins.

   b. The total cost of 25 buckets is $112.50 . How much does one bucket cost?

   Hint: choose a variable to represent what is asked (what is not known).

   c. Ann is 16 1/2 years younger than Elizabeth. When Elizabeth is 89 years old, how old will Ann be?

   Hint: choose a variable to represent what is asked (what is not known).

   d. The area of a square is 169 square centimeters. How long is its side?

   Hint: to solve the equation you get, guess and check.

   e. Two adjacent angles make a right angle together. One of the angles is 23°. What does the other angle measure?

> Two angles are adjacent if they share the same vertex and one side (they lie side-by-side).
>

2. Write an equation for each situation (even if you could solve the problem without one). Then solve the equation.

   a. Fifteen friends shared equally the cost of supplies for a party. Each person's share of the cost came to $13. How much did the supplies cost in total?

   b. Erica bought a computer for a total cost of $380.16. The sales tax was $28.16. What was the price of the computer before the sales tax was added?

   c. Henry bought 7 gallons of gasoline for $23.45. How much was the price per gallon?

   d. The perimeter of a rectangle is 1 1/2 m, and one of its sides measures 1/4 m. How long is the other side?

   e. Three adjacent angles make a straight angle together. Two of the angles are 88° and 25°. What does the third angle measure?

3. The formula *New Price* $= 0.76 \cdot 0.94^2 \cdot p$ gives us the value of a car that is three years old, where p is the original selling price. Calculate the price of a three-year-old used car for each of the given values of p.

4. (challenge) If the price of a 3-year car is $27,398.67, then what was its original selling price?

Selling Price	Price at 3 years
$24,200	
$17,500	
$36,400	

5. Can you find the *mystery expressions*?

a. I am the product of 8 and a certain sum. If you multiply the sum by 8 (using the distributive property) you will get 8b + 24. What am I?	b. Multiply me by 3, and then the result by 2, and you will get 6t − 18s + 30. What am I?

Inequalities

In an ***inequality***, we have two expressions that are separated by one of the signs $<$, $>$, $\leq$ or $\geq$.

$$\textbf{(expression)} \; < \; \textbf{(expression)}$$

As the name "*in-equality*" tells us, something is *not equal*: the two expressions are not equal.

The sign $\leq$ is read "less than or equal to." It is like the $<$ sign and $=$ sign together.
The sign $\geq$ is read "greater than or equal to." It is like the $>$ sign and $=$ sign together.

Examples of inequalities:

$6 < 9$ $\qquad$ $b \geq 5$ $\qquad\qquad\qquad$ $2x + 3 > x + 19$ $\qquad\qquad\qquad$ $\dfrac{y}{7} \geq y - 1$

Certain phrases "translate" into inequalities in mathematics.

You have to be less than 15 years old. If your age is a, then the inequality would be $a < 15$.

Don't buy more than 16 chocolate bars. This means you could buy <u>up to</u> 16 chocolate bars (16 or less). We will use the $\leq$ symbol now! Let the amount of chocolate bars be c. We can then write $c \leq 16$.

The phrase <u>at least</u> corresponds to $\geq$ (greater than or equal to).

1. Write an inequality for each phrase. You will need to choose a variable to represent the quantity in question.

   a. These shoes cost less than \$40.

   b. You have to be at least 18 years of age.

   c. There are more than 10 girls on the playground.

   d. There are at least a dozen windows.

   e. Buy at the most 5 postcards.

   f. The club is for children who are 12 years old or younger.

2. Make up a situation from real life that could be described by the given inequality.

   a. $a < 10$
   Hint: the variable a *could signify age, for example.*

   b. $g \geq 7$

   c. $p > 200$

   d. $h \leq 40$

   e. $v \geq 2,000$

We can plot or visualize inequalities that have variables **on a number line.**

The inequality $x < 9$ means that x can be any number up to 9 (but not 9). The variable x could be 1 or 1.2 or 1 1/2 or 1 8/9 or 2 or 3.5 or… There are multitudes of possibilities! We show these possibilities by coloring the whole number line up to 9. The number 9 is not included, and that is shown by drawing an open circle at 9.

What inequality would this plot illustrate? What values can x have?

This time, the circle at 5 is closed, so 5 *is* included. The inequality is $x \geq 5$. It means x can be any number greater than or equal to 5.

You can *also* write this same inequality as $5 \leq x$. We just turn the whole inequality around, so to speak.

That one is read as "5 is less than or equal to x," which means that x has to be greater than or equal to 5. The open end of the "alligator mouth" is pointing towards x in both cases, which means x is the thing that is greater than something.

3. Plot these inequalities on the number line.

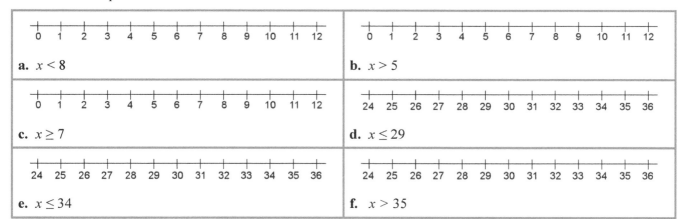

4. Write an inequality that corresponds to the number line plot.

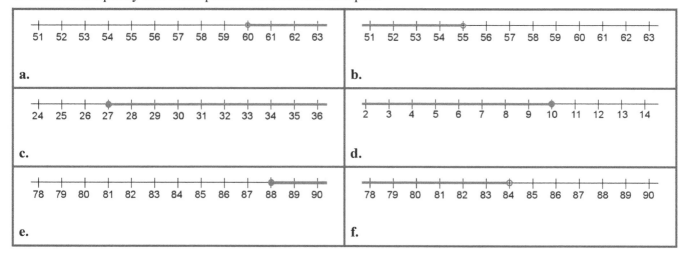

Example 1. Solve the inequality $2x + 1 < 17$ in the set $\{3, 5, 7, 9, 11\}$.

This simply means we test each number from the set, to see if it fulfils the inequality.
For example, is $2 \cdot 3 + 1$ less than 17? If so, then 3 is part of the solution.

$2 \cdot 3 + 1 = 7$, which IS less than 17.

$2 \cdot 5 + 1 = 11$, which IS less than 17.

$2 \cdot 7 + 1 = 15$, which IS less than 17.

$2 \cdot 9 + 1 = 19$, which is not less than 17.

Clearly, if we try it with 11, we will get an even bigger number than with 9, so 11 cannot be a solution.

Therefore, the solutions are 3, 5, and 7.

5. **a.** Solve the inequality $x - 5 > 8$ in the set $\{6, 9, 12, 15, 18\}$.

   b. Solve the inequality $x + 5 \leq 18$ in the set $\{1, 4, 7, 10, 13\}$.

   c. Solve the inequality $3x - 10 < 25$ in the set $\{9, 10, 11, 12, 13, 14\}$.

   d. Solve the inequality $3x - 10 \geq 25$ in the set $\{9, 10, 11, 12, 13, 14\}$.

   e. Solve the inequality $7 < y + 2$ in the set $\{3, 4, 5, 6, 7, 8\}$.

   f. Solve the inequality $12 \geq w + 2$ in the set $\{8, 10, 12, 14, 16\}$.

6. Consider the set of whole numbers $\{1, 2, 3, 4, 5, ...\}$.

   a. What solutions does the inequality $x < 6$ have in the set of whole numbers?

   b. What solutions does the inequality $x < 6$ have in the set of *even* whole numbers?

   c. What solutions does the inequality $y > 17$ have in the set of *even* whole numbers?

   d. What solutions does the inequality $y + 3 < 17$ have in the set of even whole numbers?

Optional. We solve inequalities in much the same way as equations.

Example 2. Solve $x + 2 < 9$.

For the sum $x + 2$ to be less than 9, we need the variable x to be less than 7.

$$x + 2 < 9 \,\big|\, {-2}$$

$$x < 7$$

Check by substituting *various* values of x into the original equation: do values less than 7 make it true? Do values more than or equal to 7 make it false? If so, it checks out correctly.

7. Solve these inequalities by applying the same operation to both sides.

a.	$2y < 48$	b.	$x + 8 > 42$	c.	$b - 5 \geq 50$
	$<$		$>$		$\geq$
d.	$y - 22 \leq 9$	e.	$x + 5.4 < 10.9$	f.	$20r \leq 900$

8. Solve the inequalities and plot their solution sets on a number line. Write appropriate multiples of ten under the bold tick marks.

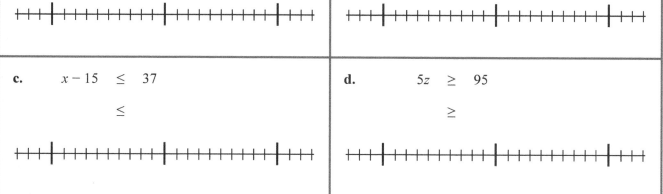

a. $3x < 30$

$<$

b. $x + 5 > 53$

$>$

c. $x - 15 \leq 37$

$\leq$

d. $5z \geq 95$

$\geq$

9. Which inequality has its solutions plotted on the number line?

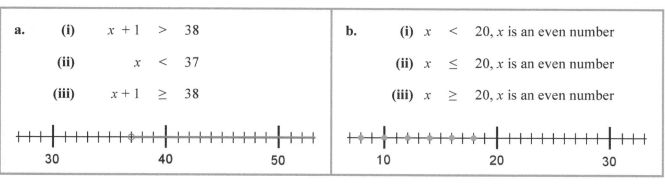

a.
(i) $x + 1 > 38$
(ii) $x < 37$
(iii) $x + 1 \geq 38$

b.
(i) $x < 20$, x is an even number
(ii) $x \leq 20$, x is an even number
(iii) $x \geq 20$, x is an even number

Using Two Variables

Often in mathematics—and in real life—we study the relationship between two variables.

Example 1. The equation $y = \frac{1}{2}x$ has two variables, y and x.

There are many values of x and y that make that equation true. For example, when x is 4, then y is $(1/2) \cdot 4 = 2$. Some of the values of x and y are listed below.

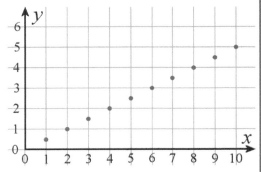

x	1	2	3	4	5
y	½	1	1 ½	2	2 ½

x	6	7	8	9	10
y	3	3 ½	4	4 ½	5

We can plot or graph these (x, y) pairs as points in the coordinate grid.
These ordered pairs actually are a **function**. We will not study the exact definition of a function here, but you can think of a function as a relationship between two variables.

In this lesson, you will study only **linear functions**. The word "linear" comes from the fact that the graphs of those functions look like a *line*. There exist many other, different kinds of functions as well.

Example 2. One towel costs $4. If you buy 17 towels, the cost is $17 \cdot \$4 = \$68$.
In this situation, we are interested in <u>two</u> <u>variables</u> whose values can change:

1. **The number of towels** a person buys is a variable. (It can vary!) Let's denote the number of towels by N.
2. **The total** cost varies according to how many towels are bought. Let C be the cost.

There is a very simple relationship between N and C: $\boxed{\text{C} = \text{N} \cdot \$4}$
(This means the total cost *is* the number of towels times $4.)

This is normally written as $\boxed{\text{C} = 4\text{N}}$ because in algebra we write the number in front of the variable (not vice versa), and we omit the multiplication sign between a number and a variable.

The table below shows some *possible* values of C and N.

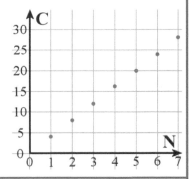

(x)	N	1	2	3	4	5	6	7	10	15	20
(y)	C	4	8	12	16	20	24	28	40	60	80

From this table, we get lots of number pairs. Some of them are plotted on the coordinate grid you see on the right.

You may have seen coordinate grids that have x and y-axis. This time we will label our axes N and C, according to the names of the variables. If this seems confusing, think of the variable N as the "x", and the variable C as the "y".

In this situation, we think of the variable N as the *independent variable*, and the variable C as the *dependent variable,* because its value *depends* on the value of N <u>according to the given equation</u> (C = 4N). In other words, we let the value of N vary (sort of independently), and the values of C are what we calculate or "observe," noticing how they depend on the value of N.

The independent variable is *always* plotted on the <u>horizontal axis</u>.

We *could* look at this situation just the opposite way also: let the cost be the independent variable, and study how the number of towels depends on that. Then, we would plot C on the horizontal axis, and calculate N using an equation that depends on C (it would be N = C/4).

1. Calculate the values of y according to the equation $y = x + 2$.

x	0	1	2	3	4	5	6	7	8
y	2	3	4						

Now, plot the points.

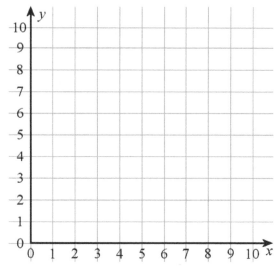

2. Calculate the values of y according to the equation $y = 8 - x$.

x	0	1	2	3	4	5	6	7	8
y	8								

Now, plot the points.

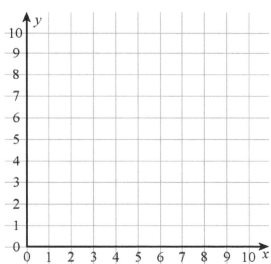

3. Calculate the values of y according to the equation $y = 2x - 1$.

x	1	2	3	4	5	6
y						

Now, plot the points.

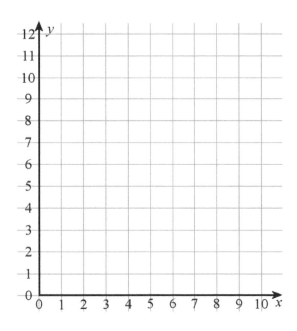

87

4. A car is traveling at a constant speed of 50 miles per hour. Consider the variables, time (*t*), measured in hours, and distance traveled (*d*), measured in miles.

   a. Fill in the table.

   b. Plot the points on the coordinate grid.

t (hours)	0	1	2	3	4	5	6
d (miles)	0	50					

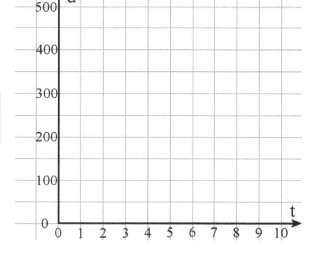

   c. Write an equation that relates *t* and *d*.

   d. Which of the two variables is the independent variable?

5. Larry gets water out of a fully-open faucet at the rate of 1 liter per 3 seconds.

   Consider the variables time (*t*), measured in seconds, and volume of water (*V*), measured in liters.

   a. Fill in the table.

   b. Plot the points on the coordinate grid.

t (sec)	0	1	2	3	4	5	6	7	8	9
V (L)										

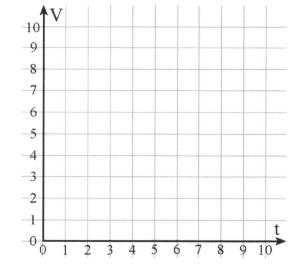

   c. Write an equation that relates *t* and *V*.

   d. Which of the two variables is the independent variable?

6. Xavier and Yvonne got 12 pieces of candy from their mother to share. They do not have to share them equally. Let us consider the candy Xavier gets (*X*), and the candy Yvonne gets (*Y*).

   a. Fill in the values of X and Y, using the already plotted points.

X							
Y							

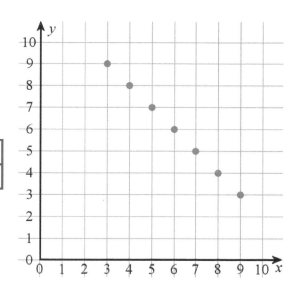

   b. Write an equation that relates *X* and *Y*.

   c. Which of the two variables is the independent variable?

7. To find a person's maximum safe heart rate during exercise (H), you can use the formula H = 220 − A, where A signifies a person's age in years. For example, the maximum safe heart rate for a 30-year-old adult would be H = 220 − 30 = 190. This result tells him that he shouldn't exercise so hard that his heart beats faster than 190 beats per minute.

a. Calculate the maximum heart rate for ages 5, 10, 15, 20, ..., 60 (every five years), and write your results in the table.

A						
H						

A						
H						

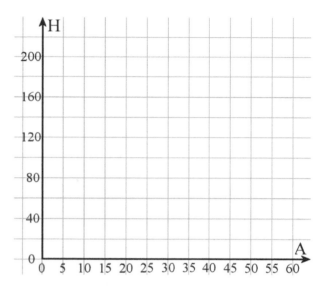

b. Plot the number pairs on the coordinate grid.

c. Which of the two variables is the dependent variable?

8. For each graph, write the number pairs in the table. Then, write an equation that relates x and y.

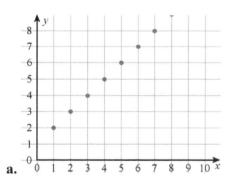

a.

x	1	2	3	4	5	6	7	8	9
y									

Equation: y = _____

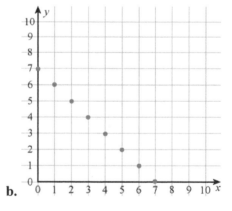

b.

x	0	1	2	3	4	5	6	7
y								

Equation: y = _____

Puzzle Corner

For each graph, write an equation that relates x and y.

a.

b.

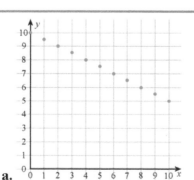

a.

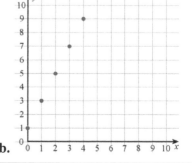

b.

Chapter 2 Mixed Review

1. **Solve.** (Powers and Exponents/Ch.1)

a. 10^5	**b.** 3^4	**c.** $10^5 \cdot 4$

2. **Fill in.** (Powers and Exponents/Ch.1)

    a. $(1.4 \text{ m})^2$ gives us the _____ of a _____ with sides _____ long.

    b. $(78 \text{ cm})^3$ gives us the _____ of a _____ with edges _____ long.

3. Three students were working on this problem:

    Margie said the answer was 9 cm, Evelyn said it is 18 cm, and Henry said it is 36 cm.

    > The area of a square is 81 cm^2. What is its perimeter?

    What do you think? Is one of them correct?
    If so, how could you show the two others that that answer is indeed the correct answer?

4. Estimate the result in your head using rounded numbers. Find the exact value using a calculator. Also, find the error of estimation. (Rounding and Estimating/Ch.1)

a. $591 \cdot 57{,}200$	**b.** $435{,}212 + 9{,}319{,}290$
Estimation:	Estimation:
Exact:	Exact:
Error of estimation:	Error of estimation:

5. Hester and Holly are going to bake cookies for the school bake sale. Below you see the recipe they want to use. A single recipe makes 2 ½ dozen cookies. *Triple* the recipe for them. (Fifth grade concepts)

Spice Cookies - makes 2 ½ dozen	
2 ¼ cups of whole wheat flour ⅓ cup of honey ½ cup of unsweetened applesauce ¾ teaspoon of nutmeg 1 ½ teaspoons of cinnamon ½ teaspoon of ground cloves ⅓ cup of raisins ¾ cup of walnuts	

6. **Write an expression.** (Terminology for the Four Operations/Ch.2)

  a. the quotient of $5s$ and 8

  b. 7 times the quantity x plus 8

  c. y less than 8

  d. the quantity x minus 8, squared

7. **Write as numbers.** (Place Value/Ch.1)

  a. 5 trillion, 51 billion, 27 thousand

  b. 21 trillion, 650 billion, 99 million, 56

  c. $6 \cdot 10^6 + 2 \cdot 10^3 + 1 \cdot 10^0$

8. **Solve. Notice carefully which operation(s) are done first.** (Order of Operations/Ch.2)

a. $4 \cdot 50 + \dfrac{310}{2} =$	**b.** $\dfrac{4{,}800}{60} - (70 - 20) =$

9. A bicycle has been discounted by 2/10 of its price, and now it costs $120. Find the price before the discount. (Lessons in Problem Solving/Ch.1)

10. **Divide. Use the space on the left to build a multiplication table for the divisor. Lastly, check.** (Review of the Four Operations/Ch.1)

	$79\overline{)5\ 6\ 2\ 7\ 9\ 0}$	$\cdot\quad 7\ 9$

Chapter 2 Review

1. Write an expression.

   a. the difference between 6 and x, squared

   b. the quotient of 5 and the sum of x and 6

   c. 3 times the quantity 5 minus p

2. Find the value of the expressions.

a. $(1 + 6)^2 + (10 - 2)^2$	**b.** $5^2 \cdot 2^3$
c. $\dfrac{21 + 6}{2 \cdot 1 + 1}$	**d.** $\dfrac{16}{2} \cdot (120 - 50)$

3. Find the value of the expressions.

a. $2x + 18$ when $x = 5$	**b.** $\dfrac{35}{z} \cdot 13$ when $z = 5$

4. Write an expression for each situation.

   a. Three friends purchased a scuba diving outfit together for p dollars.
   They shared the cost equally. How much did each person pay?

   b. You bought modeling clay for \$3 and six boxes of crayons for c dollars each.
   What was the total cost?

5. Label each thing below as an equation, inequality, or expression.

   $2x + 17$ $8 = 8$ $y < 5$ $4x - 3 = 8$ $\dfrac{4}{5}x - 16$ $4x + y^2 \geq 9$ $M = \dfrac{44 - x}{5}$

6. Simplify the expressions.

a. $t + t + t + 3$	**b.** $8d - 3d$
c. $x \cdot x \cdot x$	**d.** $12x - 6 - 6x$
e. $z \cdot z \cdot 8 \cdot z \cdot 2$	**f.** $3x^2 + 5 + 11x^2$

7. Write an expression for *both* the area and perimeter of each rectangle. Give them in simplified form.

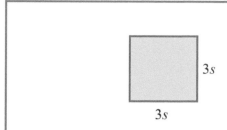

3s

3s

a. A =

P =

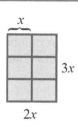

x

3x

2x

b. A =

P =

8. Multiply using the distributive property.

| **a.** $3(2x + 7) =$ | **b.** $8(9b + 5) =$ |

9. Think of the distributive property "backwards," and factor these sums.

| **a.** $5x + 10 =$ _____ $(x +$ _____ $)$ | **b.** $6y + 10 =$ _____ $($ _____ $+$ _____ $)$ |
| **c.** $24b + 4 =$ _____ $($ _____ $+$ _____ $)$ | **d.** $25w + 40 =$ _____ $($ _____ $+$ _____ $)$ |

10. Solve the equations.

| **a.** $7x = 784$ | **b.** $3 + z = 119$ | **c.** $\dfrac{x}{6} = 12$ |
| **d.** $5y + 8y = 784$ | **e.** $32 + x = 9 \cdot 40$ | **f.** $\dfrac{r}{6 + 4} = 7$ |

11. Write an equation for each situation EVEN IF you could easily solve the problem without an equation. Then solve the equation.

    a. The value of a certain number of twenty-cent coins is 1,680 cents. How many twenty-cent coins are there?

    b. The perimeter of a rectangle is 128 meters. One side is 21 meters. How long is the other side?

12. Write an inequality that corresponds to the number line plot.

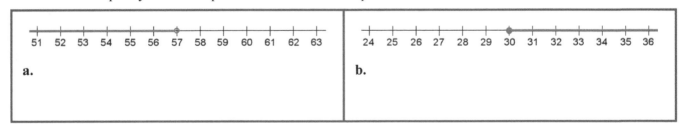

    a.

    b.

13. **a.** Solve the inequality $y + 2 > 24$ in the set $\{55, 44, 22, 23, 30\}$.

    b. What solutions does the inequality $x + 7 \leq 14$ have in the set of even whole numbers?

14. Calculate the values of y according to
the equation $y = x + 3$.

x	1	2	3	4	5	6
y						

Now, plot the points.

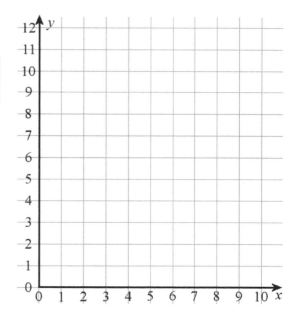

15. A train is traveling with a constant speed of 70 miles per hour. Consider the variables of time (t),
measured in hours, and the distance traveled (d), measured in miles.

a. Fill in the table.

t (hours)	0	1	2	3	4	5	6
d (miles)							

b. Plot the points on the coordinate grid.

c. Write an equation that relates t and d.

d. Which of the two variables is the independent variable?

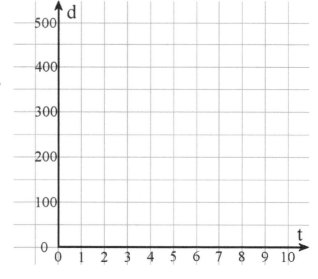

Chapter 3: Decimals
Introduction

In this chapter we study all four operations of decimals, the metric system and using decimals with measuring units. Most of these topics have already been studied in 5th grade, but in 5th grade we were using numbers with a maximum of three decimal digits. This time there is no such restriction, and the decimals used can have many more decimal digits than that.

However, since the topics are the same, consider assigning only one-fourth to one-half of the exercises initially. Monitor the student's progress and assign more if needed. The skipped problems can be used for review later.

We start out by studying place value with decimals and comparing decimals up to six decimal digits. The next several lessons contain a lot of review, just using longer decimals than in fifth grade: adding and subtracting decimals, rounding decimals, multiplying and dividing decimals, fractions and decimals, and multiplying and dividing decimals by the powers of ten.

Since the chapter focuses on restudying the mechanics of decimal arithmetic, it is a good time to stress to your student(s) the need for **accurate calculations** and for **checking one's final answer**. Notice how the lessons often ask students to estimate the answer before calculating the exact answer. Estimation can be used as a type of check for the final answer: if the final answer is far from the estimation, there is probably an error in the calculation. It can also be used to check if an answer calculated with a calculator is likely correct.

In the lessons about multiplication and division of decimals, students work both with mental math and with standard algorithms. The lessons that focus on mental math point out various patterns and shortcuts for students, helping them to see the structure and logic in math. I have also explained why the common rules (or shortcuts) for decimal multiplication and decimal division actually work, essentially providing a mathematical proof on a level that sixth graders can hopefully understand.

The last lessons deal with measuring units and the metric system, rounding out our study of decimals.

Consider mixing the lessons here with lessons from some other chapter. For example, the student could study decimals and some other topic on alternate days, or study a little of each topic each day. Such somewhat spiral usage of the curriculum can help prevent boredom, and also to help students retain the concepts better.

You will find free videos covering many topics of this chapter at https://www.mathmammoth.com/videos/.

As a reminder, check out this list of resources for challenging problems:
https://l.mathmammoth.com/challengingproblems

I recommend that you at least use the first resource listed, Math Stars Newsletters.

The Lessons in Chapter 3

	page	span
Place Value with Decimals	99	*2 pages*
Comparing Decimals	101	*2 pages*
Add and Subtract Decimals	103	*2 pages*
Rounding Decimals	105	*3 pages*
Review: Multiply and Divide Decimals Mentally	108	*2 pages*
Review: Multiply Decimals by Decimals	110	*3 pages*
Review: Long Division with Decimals	113	*2 pages*
Problem Solving with Decimals	115	*2 pages*
Fractions and Decimals	117	*3 pages*

Multiply and Divide by Powers of Ten 120   *2 pages*

Review: Divide Decimals by Decimals 122   *3 pages*

Divide Decimals by Decimals 2 125   *2 pages*

Convert Customary Measuring Units 127   *4 pages*

Convert Metric Measuring Units 131   *3 pages*

Convert Metric Measuring Units 134   *2 pages*

Chapter 3 Mixed Review 136   *2 pages*

Chapter 3 Review 138   *4 pages*

Helpful Resources on the Internet

We have compiled a list of Internet resources that match the topics in this chapter. This list of links includes web pages that offer:

- **online practice** for concepts;
- online **games**, or occasionally, printable games;
- **animations** and interactive **illustrations** of math concepts;
- **articles** that teach a math concept.

We heartily recommend you take a look at the list. Many of our customers love using these resources to supplement the bookwork. You can use the resources as you see fit for extra practice, to illustrate a concept better and even just for some fun. Enjoy!

https://l.mathmammoth.com/gr6ch3

SCAN ME

Place Value with Decimals

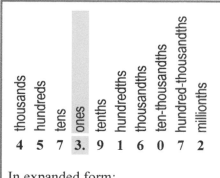

thousands	hundreds	tens	ones	tenths	hundredths	thousandths	ten-thousandths	hundred-thousandths	millionths
4	5	7	3.	9	1	6	0	7	2

The various places on the place value chart are positioned symmetrically around the ONES place.

From the ones place, we have <u>tens</u> to the left, and <u>tenths</u> to the right. Two places away are <u>hundreds</u> to the left, and <u>hundredths</u> to the right. Three places away are <u>thousands</u> to the left, and <u>thousandths</u> to the right and so on.

In expanded form:

$$4 \cdot 1{,}000 + 5 \cdot 100 + 7 \cdot 10 + 3 \cdot 1 + 9 \cdot \frac{1}{10} + 1 \cdot \frac{1}{100} + 6 \cdot \frac{1}{1{,}000} + 7 \cdot \frac{1}{100{,}000} + 2 \cdot \frac{1}{1{,}000{,}000}$$

Using decimals: $4\,000 + 500 + 70 + 3 + 0.9 + 0.01 + 0.006 + 0.00007 + 0.000002$

Example 1.

6 hundred-thousandths is $\dfrac{6}{100{,}000}$ or 0.00006.

It has <u>five</u> decimal places, the same as one hundred thousand (100,000) has <u>five</u> zeros.

Example 2.

123 ten-thousandths is $\dfrac{123}{10{,}000}$ or 0.0123.

There are <u>four</u> decimal places, the same as ten thousand (10,000) has <u>four</u> zeros.

Example 3. 7 millionths is 0.000007. It has <u>six</u> decimal places, the same as one million has six zeros.

0.000007 *also* happens to have six zeros, if you count the zero in the ones place. However, think of it as having six *decimal places*, instead, because that allows you to easily convert, for example, 453 millionths or 6,795 millionths into decimals: 0.000453 and 0.006795. They do not have six zeros, but they *do* have six decimal places.

Example 4. 465 hundredths is $\dfrac{465}{100}$.

As a decimal, it needs to have <u>two</u> decimal places because it is so many <u>hundredths</u>. (You can remember that because 100 has <u>two</u> zeros.) So it is 4.65.

Example 5.

2,180,964 ten-thousandths is $\dfrac{2{,}180{,}964}{10{,}000}$.

As a decimal, it needs to have <u>four</u> decimal places because it is so many <u>ten-thousandths</u> (and 10,000 has <u>four</u> zeros). So it is 218.0964.

---

1. Draw lines to match the expressions that have the same value.

0.00006	6 parts per thousand	$\dfrac{6}{100{,}000}$	$\dfrac{15}{100{,}000}$
0.0015	15 hundred-thousandths		
0.000006	15 ten-thousandths		$\dfrac{15}{1{,}000}$
0.00015	6 hundred-thousandths	$\dfrac{6}{1{,}000}$	
0.006	15 parts per million		$\dfrac{15}{10{,}000}$
0.000015	15 thousandths	$\dfrac{6}{100{,}000}$	
0.015	6 millionths		$\dfrac{15}{1{,}000{,}000}$

2. Write as decimals.

   a. three thousandths

   b. 34 tenths

   c. 1 and 1934 millionths

   d. 34 ten-thousandths

   e. 907 millionths

   f. 837 hundred-thousandths

   g. 52 hundredths

   h. 8 hundred-thousandths

   i. 3 and 17 thousandths

   j. 91 millionths

   k. 1 and 56 thousandths

   l. 2 and 28 319 millionths

   m. 291 ten-thousandths

   n. 4 and 5 millionths

3. Write as pure fractions, *not* as mixed numbers—that is, the numerator (the number on the top) can be greater than the denominator (the number on the bottom).

   a. 0.09

   b. 0.005

   c. 0.045

   d. 0.00371

   e. 0.02381

   f. 3.0078

   g. 2.9302

   h. 2.003814

   i. 5.3925012

   j. 0.0000031

   k. 3.294819

   l. 45.00032

4. Write in expanded form, as a sum of fractions. Follow the example.

   a. $2.67 = 2 \cdot 1 + 6 \cdot \dfrac{1}{10} + 7 \cdot \dfrac{1}{100}$

   b. 0.594

   c. 45.6

   d. 0.004923

   e. 0.00000506

5. Write as decimals.

a. $60 + 5 + \dfrac{2}{10} + \dfrac{8}{100} + \dfrac{6}{1{,}000}$	**b.** $5 + \dfrac{5}{100} + \dfrac{5}{1{,}000} + \dfrac{9}{1{,}000{,}000}$
c. $700 + \dfrac{1}{1{,}000} + \dfrac{3}{100{,}000} + \dfrac{7}{100}$	**d.** $\dfrac{1}{100} + \dfrac{3}{10{,}000} + \dfrac{4}{1{,}000{,}000}$
e. $\dfrac{9}{100} + 6 + \dfrac{3}{10{,}000} + \dfrac{5}{10}$	**f.** $\dfrac{2}{100} + 2 + \dfrac{1}{1{,}000} + \dfrac{1}{100{,}000}$

Comparing Decimals

Compare decimal numbers place by place (tenths with tenths, hundredths with hundredths, *etc.*), starting from the *biggest* place. A place value chart can help with this.

		0	.	0	0	3	8	0	5
		0	.	0	0	0	5	1	2
	T	O		te	hu	th	t-th	h-th	mi

"T" means tens.
"O" means ones.
"te" means tenths.
"hu" means hundredths.

"th" means thousandths.
"t-th" means ten-thousandths.
"h-th" means hundred-thousandths.
"mi" means millionths.

This place-by-place comparison shows that 0.003805 > 0.000512. It has 3 thousandths as its largest place value, while the other number has no thousandths.

Here is a slick trick! If you make the decimals have the same amount of decimal digits by placing zeros on the end, you can simply look at the decimal parts and compare them the same as "apples to apples" (provided of course that the whole-number parts are equal).

Example. Which is more, 6.00198 or 6.003?

Place zeros on the end of 6.003 so that it has five decimal digits: 6.003 becomes 6.00**300**. Now we compare 6.00198 to 6.00300. Since the whole-number parts are equal, and since the decimal parts are both in hundred-thousandths, you can compare the decimal parts as "numbers" in themselves:

One number has 6 and 198 hundred-thousandths, and the other one has 6 and 300 hundred-thousandths. Clearly, 300 hundred-thousandths is more than 198 hundred-thousandths, so 6.00300 is more than 6.00198.

1. Compare the numbers and write **<** , **=** , or **>**. You can use the place value charts to help.

a. 0.067 ☐ 0.0098	**b.** 0.0005 ☐ 0.005
c. 1.828 ☐ 1.0828	**d.** 2.504040 ☐ 2.505404
e. 8.00014 ☐ 8.004	**f.** 0.91701 ☐ 0.917005

2. Underline the greatest number. Use the place value charts to help.

a. 0.05 0.009 0.1	**b.** 1.04 1.2013 1.1	**c.** 0.905 0.86948 0.9
d. 0.0004 0.0000337	**e.** 9.082 9.1 9.09	**f.** 0.288391 0.284857

3. Compare the numbers and write < , = , or >.

a. 0.0087 ☐ 0.0009   **b.** 1.00583 ☐ 1.002301   **c.** 1.270038 ☐ 1.27011

d. 0.000002 ☐ 0.0000004   **e.** 26 millionths ☐ 0.00001   **f.** 450 thousandths ☐ 3 tenths

4. **a.** Mark these decimals on the number line: 0.01   0.012   0.005   0.03   0.028   0.009   0.017

b. What number is exactly at the midpoint of 0 and 0.01?

c. What number is exactly at the midpoint of 0.01 and 0.02?

d. What number is exactly at the midpoint of 0 and 0.001?

e. What number is exactly at the midpoint of 0.001 and 0.002?

5. Write in order from the smallest to the largest.

a. 0.293 0.31 0.0491	**b.** 1.304 1.34 1.043
c. 3.0098 3.00028 3.0089	**d.** 0.000023 0.000003 0.00002
e. 1.107 1.0987 1.098	**f.** 0.0456 0.04 0.045

6. Calculate without a calculator.

a. $0.4 + \dfrac{8}{1,000}$ **b.** $0.2 + \dfrac{7}{100}$ **c.** $4.001 + \dfrac{7}{1,000}$ **d.** $\dfrac{5}{1,000} + 0.06$

7. Add a tenth, a hundredth, or a thousandth. Be careful!

Number	0.4	0.35	0.027	1.297	5.99	0.606
+ 0.1						
+ 0.01						
+ 0.001						

Add and Subtract Decimals

Here is a "trick" to help you with decimal addition and subtraction:

Give all of the addends the same amount of decimal digits by "tagging" zeros onto the ends.

For example, in the problem $0.024 + 0.1 + 0.05$, if we place two zeros onto the end of 0.1 and one zero onto the end of 0.05, then all of the addends will have three decimal digits. (see the box on the top right) →

Now, you can simply add how many thousandths each number has: $24 + 100 + 50 = 174$. The answer has three decimals, so it is 0.174.

The column-addition on the right shows the same principle. →

$$
\begin{array}{ccc}
0.024 & + 0.1 & + 0.05 \\
\downarrow & \downarrow & \downarrow \\
0.024 & + 0.100 & + 0.050 = 0.174
\end{array}
$$

$$
\begin{array}{r}
0.0\ 2\ 4 \\
0.1\ 0\ 0 \\
+\ 0.0\ 5\ 0 \\
\hline
0.1\ 7\ 4
\end{array}
$$

1. Write the decimal that is more or less than the given decimal by the specified amount.

a.

O		t	h	th	t-th
0	.	0	0	2	

1 tenth more: _____

1 thousandth less: _____

1 ten-thousandth more: _____

b.

O		t	h	th	t-th	h-th
0	.	8	5			

2 hundredths less: _____

2 ten-thousandths more: _____

2 hundred-thousandths more: _____

2. Add.

a. $0.2 + 0.8 =$	**d.** $0.03 + 0.06 =$	**g.** $0.09 + 0.007 =$
b. $0.2 + 0.08 =$	**e.** $0.03 + 0.0006 =$	**h.** $0.9 + 0.007 =$
c. $0.2 + 0.0008 =$	**f.** $0.03 + 0.00006 =$	**i.** $0.00009 + 0.007 =$

3. Add or subtract in your head. First, change the fraction into a decimal.

a. $1\frac{3}{10} + 0.56$	**b.** $0.2 + \frac{27}{100}$	**c.** $3.19 + \frac{5}{10}$	**d.** $2\frac{289}{1,000} - 0.1$

4. Continue the sequences for six more numbers. Use mental math.

   a. 0.25, 0.28, 0.31,

   b. 3.275, 3.28, 3.285,

5. Two of these calculations are in error. Find them and explain why they are wrong.

a. $0.15 + 0.2 = 0.17$	**b.** $1.06 + 0.04 = 1.1$	**c.** $0.9 - 0.08 = 0.1$

6. Find the value of the expression $0.5 - y$ when

a. $y = 0.2$	**b.** $y = 0.02$	**c.** $y = 0.002$

7. Calculate in columns. You may use extra (grid) paper. Remember to line up the decimal points.
   But first, *estimate* the answer. For estimating, round the numbers in such a way that you can calculate in
   your head. If your final answer is far from your estimate, you may have made an error.

a. $6.907 - 4.80056$	**b.** $2 + 9.082 + 0.038284 + 4.5028$	**c.** $410 - 25.6 - 4.59384$
Estimate: _____	Estimate: _____	Estimate: _____

8. First change the fractions to decimals. Then calculate.

a. $\dfrac{4}{10,000} + \dfrac{4}{100}$	**b.** $\dfrac{900}{100} + \dfrac{9}{10,000} - \dfrac{1}{2}$

Puzzle Corner

Solve the equation: $3.08 - x - 0.39192 = 0.00311$

Rounding Decimals

Let's review the rounding rules for decimals once again. This time you will practice with "longer" decimals!

1. Find the digit that you are rounding to. You can draw a "cut-off line" after that digit to help you.

2. Look at the *next smaller* place (the digit after that). If that digit is 4 or less, round down. If it is 5 or more, round up.

3. If you round *up*, the digit in the place that you are rounding to will go up by 1. If you round *down*, that digit stays the same.

4. All the digits *after* the place you are rounding to become zeros... BUT, **if those are decimal digits, we do not write them!** We simply cut off those decimal digits.

For example, $0.274 | 91 \approx 0.275$.

Rounding to the nearest ten:
Look at the ones digit.

$$3\,2\,|\,\mathbf{5}\,.\,0\,6\,7\,2\,4\,8 \approx 3\,3\,0$$

Rounding to the nearest hundredth:
Look at the thousandths digit.

$$3\,2\,5\,.\,0\,6\,|\,7\,2\,4\,8 \approx 3\,2\,5\,.\,0\,7$$

Rounding to the nearest ten-thousandth:
Look at the hundred-thousandths digit.

$$3\,2\,5\,.\,0\,6\,7\,2\,|\,4\,8 \approx 3\,2\,5\,.\,0\,6\,7\,2$$

1. Round to the place (digit) just before the dashed line.

a. $2.6|72 \approx$	**b.** $3.055|23$	**c.** $2.26|54$	**d.** $0.048|97$

2. Round to the nearest hundredth.

a. 7.248	**b.** 0.02499	**c.** 1.358	**d.** 4.97611

3. Round to the nearest thousandth.

a. 7.249392	**b.** 0.02684	**c.** 1.39452	**d.** 4.908472

4. Jack bought coffee for \$1.80, rolls for \$0.95, a meal for \$6.75 and two "kids' meals" for \$6.15 each.

   a. Estimate the total cost by rounding the numbers to the nearest dollar.

   b. Estimate Jack's change from \$30.

   c. Find the exact cost and the error of estimation.

Example 1. Rounding 3.29971 to the nearest thousandth, we get:

$$3.299\,|71 \approx 3.300$$

It is as if we increase the "number" 299 to 300.

NOTICE: we MUST keep the thousandths and hundredths digits in the rounded number, and NOT write the answer as 3.3.

Why? We are rounding to the _nearest thousandth_ so the rounded answer _has_ to have the thousandths digit. Otherwise, if it was written as 3.3, you might think we had rounded it to the nearest tenth!

Example 2. Rounding 109.9984 to the nearest hundredth:

$$109.99\,|84 \approx 110.00$$

It is as if we increase the "number" 0999 to 1,000.

Notice that the answer is written as 110.00, **leaving zeros in the tenths and hundredths places.**

If you wrote it as 110, it would look like it was rounded to the nearest one or nearest ten, and not to to the nearest hundredth.

Those zeros at the end of a decimal number (such as the zeros in 3.300) are called **trailing zeros**. Normally, we do not write trailing zeros after a decimal because they do not change the value of the decimal (4.500 = 4.5). However, we do write them when making a claim about _how accurate_ a number is.

For example, the numbers 0.5, 0.50 and 0.500 _are not equally accurate_. The first, 0.5, is accurate to the nearest tenth. Maybe you rounded 0.458 to the nearest tenth and got 0.5. Maybe you rounded 0.548 to the nearest tenth and got 0.5. We don't know what the original number was - but we DO know it is greater than or equal to 0.45 and less than 0.55.

Similarly, 0.50 is accurate to the nearest hundredth, and 0.500 is accurate to the nearest thousandth.

---

5. Round to the digit just before the dashed line.

a. 0.9|52 ≈	**b.** 2.059|63 ≈	**c.** 6.19|98 ≈
d. 0.049|97 ≈	**e.** 7.240|392 ≈	**f.** 0.199|7 ≈
g. 3.99|95 ≈	**h.** 0.099|9643 ≈	**i.** 0.0090|278 ≈

6. Round the decimals to the underlined place.

a. 0.383<u>9</u>9483	**b.** 2.3<u>9</u>187	**c.** 0.03899<u>7</u>8
d. 93<u>8</u>.259	**e.** 70<u>9</u>.609	**f.** 99<u>9</u>.83

7. Round to...

Number:	0.289940	1.293854	2.5949405	0.394040	2.299775
…three decimals					
…four decimals					
…five decimals					

8. Round the numbers to *two decimal digits*, and use the rounded numbers to *estimate* the answer.
   Then calculate the exact answer. Compare your final answer to your estimation. If your final answer differs
   a lot from your estimation, you might have made an error in the calculation.

a. 0.1539204 + 0.23609

Estimate: *0.15 + 0.24 = 0.39*

Exact:
$$
\begin{array}{r}
0.1539204 \\
+\,0.23609 \\
\hline
\end{array}
$$

b. 1.39821 + 0.2831

Estimate:

Exact:

c. 3.4822 + 3 − 4.5078

Estimate:

Exact:

d. 2.917328 − 0.302849 − 1.0549

Estimate:

Exact:

Who am I?

" I have three decimal digits. When rounded to the nearest whole number, I become 5.
When rounded to the nearest tenth, I become 5.4. When rounded to the nearest hundredth,
I get to be 5.45. Lastly… my digits add up to 21."

Review: Multiply and Divide Decimals Mentally

One factor is a whole number. Think of multiplication without the decimal point.	
6 · 0.2 = ???	**7 · 0.0009 = ???**
This is six times two tenths. First, multiply 6 · 2 = 12. The answer to 6 times 2 _tenths_ will be _twelve tenths_, which is 1.2.	This is 7 times 9 _ten-thousandths_. First, multiply 7 · 9 = 63 in your head. The answer will be _63 ten-thousandths_, which is 0.0063.
Notice the answer 1.2 has the same amount of decimal digits as 0.2: both contain _tenths_.	Notice the answer 0.0063 has the same amount of decimal digits as 0.0009: both contain _ten-thousandths_.

1. Find the values using mental math. Compare the problems, and notice the patterns.

a.	b.	c.	d.
7 · 0.6 =	4 · 1.5 =	3 · 0.05 =	9 · 0.8 =
7 · 0.06 =	4 · 0.15 =	3 · 0.005 =	9 · 0.008 =
7 · 0.006 =	4 · 0.0015 =	3 · 0.0005 =	9 · 0.00008 =

The divisor is a whole number. Think of equal sharing. Check by multiplying.	
0.26 ÷ 2 = ???	**2.403 ÷ 3 = ????**
Think: 26 hundredths is divided between two people. It is like sharing apples—we simply have hundredths instead of apples. Each person gets 13 hundredths. $$0.26 \div 2 = 0.13$$ This is also verified by multiplication: $$2 \cdot 0.13 = 0.26$$	We can divide in parts: 1) First, 2.4 divided by 3 gives 0.8. 2) Then, 0.003 ÷ 3 is 0.001. The total answer is 0.801. Check: 3 · 0.801 = 3 · 0.8 + 3 · 0.001 = 2.4 + 0.003 = 2.403

2. Divide. For each division, write a corresponding multiplication sentence.

a.	b.	c.	d.
0.36 ÷ 4 =	3.5 ÷ 7 =	0.008 ÷ 2 =	0.099 ÷ 9 =
e.	**f.**	**g.**	**h.**
0.0046 ÷ 2 =	0.0024 ÷ 3 =	0.00049 ÷ 7 =	0.144 ÷ 12 =

Think: How many times does it fit?	
0.024 ÷ 0.002 = ???	**0.9 ÷ 0.01 = ????**
Think: How many times does 0.002 fit into 0.024? Or how many times do 2 thousandths fit into 24 thousandths? The answer is 12 times. So, 0.024 ÷ 0.002 = 12. Check: 12 · 0.002 = 0.024	Write 0.9 as 0.90 so that the two numbers have the same amount of decimals. We get 0.90 ÷ 0.01. How many times does one hundredth go into ninety hundredths? Clearly, 90 times, so 0.90 ÷ 0.01 = 90. Check: 90 · 0.01 = 90 hundredths = 0.90 = 0.9

3. Divide. For each division, write a corresponding multiplication sentence.

a. 0.36 ÷ 0.06 =	**b.** 1.8 ÷ 0.2 =	**c.** 0.054 ÷ 0.006 =

4. Divide in your head. Think: How many times does the divisor go into the dividend?

a. 4 ÷ 0.5 =	**b.** 2 ÷ 0.4 =	**c.** 0.56 ÷ 0.07 =
d. 0.0012 ÷ 0.0004 =	**e.** 0.015 ÷ 0.005 =	**f.** 0.0032 ÷ 0.0008 =

5. Add zeros to the dividend, so that the dividend and divisor have the same amount of decimal digits, and then divide. Check by multiplication.

a. 0.30 ÷ 0.15 = 2 2 · 0.15 = 0.30	**b.** 0.04 ÷ 0.005 =	**c.** 0.4 ÷ 0.02 =
d. 0.6 ÷ 0.002 =	**e.** 0.7 ÷ 0.01 =	**f.** 0.008 ÷ 0.00002 =

6. **a.** How many 0.3 m pieces can you get out of a board that is 15.3 meters long?

   b. Ann, Lisa and Joanne shared equally the cost for a dinner that cost $63.90. What was each person's share? Use mental math.

7. Divide. Use mental math.

a. 2.5 ÷ 5	**b.** 3 ÷ 0.6 =	**c.** 1.02 ÷ 2
d. 0.048 ÷ 0.008	**e.** 0.6 ÷ 0.02	**f.** 0.0056 ÷ 7
g. 4.018 ÷ 2	**h.** 0.0306 ÷ 3	**i.** 0.5055 ÷ 5

Review: Multiply Decimals by Decimals

The shortcut to decimal multiplication
1) Multiply as if there were no decimal points.
2) Place the decimal point in the answer. The number of decimal digits in the answer is exactly the sum of the number of decimal digits in each of the factors.

0.9 · 0.07	**1.02 · 0.002 · 0.2**
Multiply 9 · 7 = 63. The two factors 0.9 and 0.07 have one and two decimal digits, respectively. So the answer will have three decimal digits. The answer is 0.063.	Multiply without decimal points: 102 · 2 · 2 = 408. Since 1.02 has two, 0.002 has three, and 0.2 has one decimal digit, the answer needs *six*: 1.02 · 0.002 · 0.2 = 0.000408.

1. Multiply.

a. $0.2 \cdot 0.8 =$	**b.** $0.7 \cdot 0.12 =$	**c.** $0.03 \cdot 0.9 =$
d. $0.004 \cdot 0.5 =$	**e.** $0.02 \cdot 0.0009 =$	**f.** $0.011 \cdot 0.06 =$

2. Multiply.

a. $1.1 \cdot 0.02 \cdot 0.5 =$	**d.** $0.3 \cdot 4 \cdot 0.002 =$
b. $0.3 \cdot 0.07 \cdot 0.2 =$	**e.** $0.3 \cdot 0.3 \cdot 0.3 =$
c. $5 \cdot 0.02 \cdot 0.004 =$	**f.** $4 \cdot 0.4 \cdot 0.0005 =$

3. Find the total cost using mental math.

    a. You bought 0.3 meters of rope that cost $3.50 per meter.

    b. You bought 1.2 kg of dates that cost $50 per kilogram.

    c. You bought 2.5 liters of tea that costs $0.80 per liter.

4. Find the value of each expression if $k = 0.008$ and $s = 0.3$.

a. k^2	**b.** $sk + 1$	**c.** $3k + s$

Why does it work that way?

Let's compare decimal and fraction multiplication:

$$0.7 \cdot 0.009 = 0.0063$$

$$\downarrow \qquad \downarrow \qquad \qquad \downarrow$$

$$\frac{7}{10} \cdot \frac{9}{1,000} = \frac{63}{10,000}$$

(Remember: in fraction multiplication, we simply multiply the "top" numbers to get the numerator, and we multiply the bottom numbers to get the denominator.)

Notice what happens in the **denominators**: we multiply 10 times 1,000 and get 10,000.

When we write a decimal as a fraction, it always has a denominator that is a power of ten (1 followed by zeros). The denominator tells us how many decimal digits there are in the corresponding decimal: if you have one decimal digit, you have so many *tenths*, so the denominator is *ten* (10 has one zero).

If you have three decimal digits, you have thousandths, and the denominator is one thousand (1,000 has three zeros). And so on. The number of decimal digits in the decimal tells us how many zeros the number in the denominator has.

When you multiply the denominators, you get a new denominator, which is also a power of ten and has *exactly as many zeros* as there were in the two denominators in total! Of course, that again tells us how many decimal digits there are in the answer!

Look at another example. The number of zeros corresponds to the number of decimal digits:

$$0.02 \cdot 0.0008 = 0.000016$$

$$\downarrow \qquad \quad \downarrow \qquad \qquad \downarrow$$

$$\frac{2}{100} \cdot \frac{8}{10,000} = \frac{16}{1,000,000}$$

I hope you can see this! It is really neat!

5. Write the decimals as fractions and multiply both.

a. $0.4 \cdot 0.03 =$	**b.** $0.009 \cdot 0.3 =$	**c.** $0.011 \cdot 0.0006 =$
$\downarrow \qquad \downarrow \qquad \downarrow$	$\downarrow \qquad \downarrow \qquad \downarrow$	$\downarrow \qquad \downarrow \qquad \downarrow$
d. $1.1 \cdot 0.002 =$	**e.** $0.21 \cdot 0.0004 =$	**f.** $0.005 \cdot 0.005 =$
$\downarrow \qquad \downarrow \qquad \downarrow$	$\downarrow \qquad \downarrow \qquad \downarrow$	$\downarrow \qquad \downarrow \qquad \downarrow$

6. Make up three decimal multiplications with a product (answer) of 0.0008, without using whole numbers as factors.

7. Solve the equations.

a. $\dfrac{z}{0.5} = 0.07$	**b.** $3z = 0.00033$	**c.** $0.9d = 0.72$

You can use long multiplication (the multiplication algorithm) with decimal numbers as well.

Multiply as if there were no decimal points. Put a decimal point in the answer so that the answer has as many decimal places (digits) as there were in all of the factors.

$$
\begin{array}{r}
3\ 4 \\
0.2\ 4\ 7 \\
\cdot\quad\ \ 1.7 \\
\hline
1\ 7\ 2\ 9 \\
+\ 2\ 4\ 7\ 0 \\
\hline
0.4\ 1\ 9\ 9
\end{array}
$$

← three decimal places
← one decimal place

← four decimal places

To check if your answer is reasonable, estimate it by rounding the factors in such a way that you can multiply in your head: $0.247 \cdot 1.7 \approx 0.2 \cdot 2 = 0.4$, which is close to our answer 0.4199 above. So it is reasonable.

8. First, estimate the result by rounding the factors in such a manner that you can multiply in your head. (There are no hard-and-fast rules on how to round, as it depends on your mental multiplication skills.) Then, find the exact answer. Lastly, **check if your answer is reasonable** by comparing your answer to the estimate.

a. $0.37 \cdot 0.91$

Estimate: _____

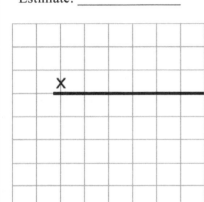

b. $1.205 \cdot 0.51$

Estimate: _____

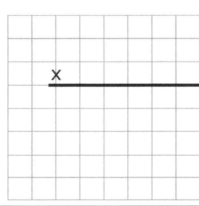

c. $3.93 \cdot 0.043$

Estimate: _____

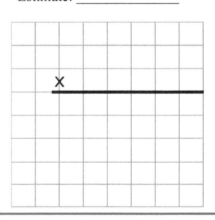

9. If $12{,}345 \cdot 6{,}789 = 83{,}810{,}205$, then how much is

a. $12.345 \cdot 678.9$

b. $123.45 \cdot 0.6789$

c. $1.2345 \cdot 67.89$

10. An image on the computer is 800 by 1,000 pixels (width and height). You increase the size of the image until both the width and the height become 1.4 times as long. What are the new dimensions of the image?

11. Multiply in your notebook. First estimate the answer by rounding the factors.

a. $0.455 \cdot 6.4 =$ _____   Estimate: _____ · _____ = _____

b. $3.08 \cdot 0.0034 =$ _____   Estimate: _____ · _____ = _____

Puzzle Corner

Solve 0.1^{11}.

Hint: Investigate the pattern in the number of zeros in the powers of 0.1.

Review: Long Division with Decimals

To do long division with decimals, divide as though there were no decimal point. Then put the decimal point into the quotient *at the same place* where it is in the dividend.

```
  0 1.5 4
8)1 2.3 2
  8
  4 3
 -4 0
    3 2
   -3 2
      0
```

Check:

```
    4 3
    1.5 4
  ·   8
1 2.3 2
```

If the division does not come out even, you can add decimal zeros to the dividend and continue to divide. When you stop dividing, give the answer as a rounded number.

In the example at the right, the quotient is carried out to *four* decimal places, so we round the answer to *three* places: $2 \div 11 \approx 0.182$.

```
   0.1 8 1 8
11)2.0 0 0 0
   1 1
     9 0
    -8 8
       2 0
      -1 1
         9 0
        -8 8
           2
```

1. Divide. Check each division result with multiplication.

a. 5)7.8 5

b. 3)2.0 6 1

c. 7)6.1 5 7

2. Divide. Round the answer to three decimals.

a. 6)7.1 0 0 0

b. 3)1.3 0 0 0

c. 7)2.5 0 9 0

3. Divide. Add a decimal point and decimal zeros to the dividend. If the division does not come out exactly, then round the answer to three decimals.

a. $11\overline{)7}$

b. $8\overline{)21}$

c. $5\overline{)14.2}$

d. $9\overline{)45.08}$

e. $14\overline{)48.44}$

f. $23\overline{)52.7}$

4. Divide using long division. If the division is not exact, round the answer to three decimals.

a. $4.1314 \div 7$

b. $46.08 \div 9$

c. $0.342 \div 6$

d. $125 \div 13$

e. $212.5 \div 23$

f. $460 \div 51$

Problem Solving with Decimals

Example 1. Martha jogs 0.8 miles every day. How many days will it take for her to jog a distance of 20 miles?

We could divide 20 miles by 0.8 miles to find out how many times 0.8 "fits" into 20. However, there is also another way: we can solve it with *mental math*.

Notice, 0.8 goes evenly into 4, and 4 goes evenly into 20.

0.8 fits five times into 4 (because 5 × 0.8 = 4). And, 4 fits five times into 20.

So, 0.8 fits into 20 exactly 5 × 5 = 25 times.

Martha will have jogged 20 miles in 25 days.

Example 2. If you divide a paper that is 8.5 inches wide into 3 equally-wide columns, how wide are the columns?

Divide the 8.5 inches by three. It is reasonable to give the answer to *two* decimal places, so divide until there are *three* decimals in the quotient, and then round to the nearest hundredth.

8.5 ÷ 3 ≈ 2.83, so the parts are about 2.83 inches wide.

```
        2.8 3 3
   3 )8.5 0 0
     -6
       2 5
      -2 4
          1 0
          -  9
            1 0
            - 0 9
                1
```

In all of the problems, give your answer to a meaningful accuracy, especially when the division is not even.

1. Jack, John and Jerry shared a prize of $200 equally. How much did each one get?

2. A student textbook weighs 0.4 kg. How many of those can you pack into a suitcase so that the total weight is 18 kg?

3. These are the quiz results of the Spanish class:
   21 15 18 29 19 34 39 21 11 8 15 28 15 11 12.
   Find the average.

4. Find the area and perimeter of this shape.

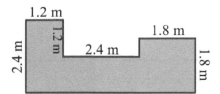

5. Kitchen Delight makes blenders. Each blender
   weighs 1.2 kg. The shipping company allows no
   more than 40 kg of weight in each shipping crate.
   How many blenders can be packed into each
   shipping crate?

6. Find the unit prices for the following items. Round to the nearest cent. Use blank paper for calculations.

Item and price	Unit price	What would this cost...?	
32 oz of orange juice for $3.65		12 oz of orange juice	
3 lb of chicken for $3.24		5.7 lb of chicken	
4 lb of bananas for $1.99		2.5 lb of bananas	

Fractions and Decimals

You already know how to change decimals to fractions. The number of decimal digits tells you the denominator —it is always a power of ten with as many zeros as you have decimal digits. For the numerator, just copy all the digits from the number.

Example: $3.0928 = \dfrac{30,928}{10,000}$

You can also write this as a mixed number, in which case you take the whole number part from the decimal, and the actual decimal digits form the numerator:

$15.30599 = \dfrac{1,530,599}{100,000} = 15\dfrac{30,599}{100,000}$

1. Write as fractions.

a. 0.09	**b.** 0.005	**c.** 0.045
d. 0.00371	**e.** 0.02381	**f.** 0.0000031

2. Write as fractions and also as mixed numbers.

a. 2.9302	**b.** 2.003814
c. 5.3925012	**d.** 3.0078
e. 3.294819	**f.** 45.00032

When changing a **fraction into a decimal**, we have several tools in our "toolbox."

Tool 1. If the denominator of a fraction is already a power of ten, there is not much to do but to write it as a decimal. The number of zeros in the power of ten tells you the number of decimal digits you need.

$\dfrac{3}{10} = 0.3$　　$\dfrac{451,593}{10,000} = 45.1593$

3. Write as decimals.

a. $\dfrac{36}{100}$	**b.** $\dfrac{5,009}{1,000}$	**c.** $1\dfrac{45}{1,000}$
d. $\dfrac{3,908}{10,000}$	**e.** $2\dfrac{593}{100,000}$	**f.** $\dfrac{5,903}{1,000,000}$
g. $\dfrac{45,039,034}{1,000,000}$	**h.** $\dfrac{435,112}{10,000}$	**i.** $\dfrac{450,683}{100,000}$

Tool 2. With some fractions, you can find an equivalent fraction with a denominator of 10, 100, 1,000, *etc.* and then write the fraction as a decimal.	$\dfrac{27}{30} \overset{\div 3}{=} \dfrac{9}{10} = 0.9$ (÷ 3)	$\dfrac{66}{200} \overset{\div 2}{=} \dfrac{33}{100} = 0.33$ (÷ 2)	$\dfrac{3}{8} \overset{\cdot\,125}{=} \dfrac{375}{1,000} = 0.375$ (· 125)

4. Write as decimals. Think of the equivalent fraction that has a denominator of 10, 100, or 1,000.

a. $\dfrac{1}{5}$	**b.** $\dfrac{1}{8}$	**c.** $1\dfrac{1}{20}$
d. $3\dfrac{9}{25}$	**e.** $\dfrac{12}{200}$	**f.** $8\dfrac{3}{4}$
g. $4\dfrac{3}{5}$	**h.** $\dfrac{13}{20}$	**i.** $\dfrac{7}{8}$
j. $\dfrac{11}{125}$	**k.** $\dfrac{24}{400}$	**l.** $\dfrac{95}{500}$

5. In these problems, you see both fractions and decimals. Either change the decimal into a fraction, or vice versa. You decide which way is easier! Then, calculate in your head.

a. $0.2 + \dfrac{1}{4}$	**b.** $0.34 + 1\dfrac{1}{5}$	**c.** $2\dfrac{3}{5} + 1.3$	**d.** $\dfrac{5}{8} - 0.09$
e. $0.02 + \dfrac{3}{4}$	**f.** $1.9 + 3\dfrac{1}{8}$	**g.** $\dfrac{14}{20} - 0.23$	**h.** $\dfrac{18}{25} + 0.07$

Tool 3. Most of the time, in order to change a fraction to a decimal, you simply treat the fraction as a division problem and divide (with a calculator or long division).	$\dfrac{5}{6} = 5 \div 6 = 0.83333... \approx 0.83$

6. Write the fractions as decimals. Use long division on blank paper. Give your answers to three decimal digits.

a. $\dfrac{2}{9} =$	**b.** $\dfrac{3}{7} =$	**c.** $\dfrac{7}{16} =$

7. Use a calculator to write these fractions as decimals. Give your answers to three decimal digits.

a. $\dfrac{1}{11} =$	**b.** $\dfrac{3}{23} =$	**c.** $\dfrac{47}{56} =$

8. Label the bold tick marks on the number line as "0," "1" and "2." Then mark the following numbers on it where they belong.

$$0.2, \quad \frac{1}{4}, \quad 0.65, \quad 1\frac{1}{3}, \quad 0.04, \quad \frac{2}{5}, \quad 1.22, \quad 1\frac{3}{4}, \quad 1.95, \quad 1\frac{4}{5}$$

9. One bag of milk powder contains 900 g. Another contains 3/4 kg.
   What is the combined weight of the two?

10. Flax seed costs $11.45 per kilogram. Sally bought 1.75 kg of it.
    Calculate the total price of Sally's purchase (in dollars and cents).

11. Explain two different ways to calculate the price of 3/8 of a liter of oil, if one liter costs $12.95.
    You do not have to calculate the price; just explain or show two ways of *how* to do it.

12. A foundation for a building measures 14 ¾ m by 20 ⅖ m.
    Find its area in square meters, as a decimal.

13. Anna lives in Australia, and her friend Cindy lives in the USA. Cindy said that she used 1 ¾ pounds of beef for a certain dish. Anna needs to know this amount in grams, but also, she wants to make only ⅔ of the recipe since her family is smaller. One pound is 454 grams. Find how much beef, in grams, Anna needs to make the dish for her family.

Multiply and Divide by Powers of Ten

When you multiply a decimal number by a power of ten (10, 100, 1,000 and so on), move the decimal point to the *right* as many steps, or places, as there are zeros in the factor 10, 100, 1,000, or so on.

$100 \cdot 0.045 = 4.5$	$1{,}000 \cdot 2.860 = 2860. = 2{,}860$	$10^5 \cdot 0.05400 = 5{,}400$
Move the decimal point two steps to the right because 100 has two zeros.	Move the decimal point three steps to the right. Write a zero at the end of 0.286, so the decimal point can "jump over" to that place.	10^5 has five zeros. Move the decimal point five steps to the right. Write zeros at the end of 0.054 so the decimal point can be moved over those places.

1. Multiply decimals by powers of ten.

a.	b.	c.
$10 \cdot 3.84 =$	$100 \cdot 0.09 =$	$10{,}000 \cdot 3.84 =$
$1{,}000 \cdot 3.84 =$	$0.594 \cdot 10{,}000 =$	$0.0038 \cdot 1{,}000 =$

d.	e.	f.
$10^3 \cdot 1.09 =$	$10^3 \cdot 0.0075 =$	$10^7 \cdot 0.0021 =$
$10^4 \cdot 1.09 =$	$10^5 \cdot 0.0075 =$	$10^6 \cdot 4.8 =$

With division by a power of ten, you move the decimal point to the *left* as many steps as there are zeros in the divisor.

$00.28 \div 10 = 0.028$	$0012.0 \div 1{,}000 = 0.012$	$000256.2 \div 10^5 = 0.002562$
Move the decimal point one step to the left.	Move the decimal point three steps to the left. Write zeros in front of the number to help.	Move the decimal point five steps to the left. Again, write zeros in front.

2. Divide the decimals by powers of ten.

a.	b.	c.
$1.5 \div 10 =$	$1.08 \div 100 =$	$56 \div 10 =$
$0.43 \div 10 =$	$2.3 \div 100 =$	$56 \div 1{,}000 =$

d.	e.	f.
$0.69 \div 10^3 =$	$2.9 \div 10^5 =$	$67.8 \div 100 =$
$51.0 \div 10^4 =$	$4{,}500 \div 10^6 =$	$251 \div 10^4 =$

Another shortcut! If you can easily figure out where one of the digits goes, the others "follow" or are just placed around it.

Example 1.	**Example 2.**	**Example 3.**
When you multiply by 1,000, the digit in the thousand*ths* place will become the digit in the ones place. In 1,000 · 0.056, six needs to go in the ones place, so the answer is 56.	In the problem 100 · 54.9, the four in the ones place must become four hundred, so the answer must be 5,490.	____ · 7.048 = 704.8. Here, 7 in the ones place became 700. The missing factor must be 100!

3. Multiply or divide.

a.	b.	c.
0.23 ÷ 100 =	1,000 · 97.201 =	10^6 · 34.2958 =
1,400 ÷ 10,000 =	10^6 · 0.004835 =	10^5 · 0.00293 =
3.892 ÷ 1,000 =	10^4 · 3.49284 =	10^7 · 2.19304 =

4. Find the missing factor or divisor.

a. 0.15 · _____ = 15 0.932 · _____ = 9.32	**b.** _____ · 30.4 = 3,040 _____ · 5.5 = 5,500
c. 0.029 · _____ = 2,900 0.0006 · _____ = 600	**d.** _____ · 0.34 = 34,000 _____ · 0.00478 = 0.478

e. $\dfrac{17}{\rule{2cm}{0.4pt}}$ = 0.017	**f.** $\dfrac{2.3}{\rule{2cm}{0.4pt}}$ = 0.023	**g.** $\dfrac{412}{\rule{2cm}{0.4pt}}$ = 4.12	**h.** $\dfrac{0.58}{\rule{2cm}{0.4pt}}$ = 0.058

Why does this SHORTCUT work?

When 0.01 (one hundredth) is multiplied by ten, we get ten hundredths, which is equal to one tenth. In other words, 10 · 0.01 = 0.1.

T	O	t	h	th
	.	0	1	

The entire number 0.01 moved one "slot" to the left on the place value chart →
This *looks like* moving the decimal point in the number to the right.

T	O	t	h	th
	.	1		

Multiplying two tenths by 100 is the same as multiplying it by 10, and then by 10 again. Ten times 0.2 gives us two, and ten times that gives us 20.

T	O	t	h	th
	.	2		

T	O	t	h	th
2	0	.		

Again, that 2 moves two "slots" to the left in the place value chart, but it looks like the decimal point in the number 0.2 moved two steps to the right.

When 3.915 is multiplied by 100, each part of that number (3 ones, 9 tenths, 1 hundredth, 5 thousandths) is multiplied by 100 and moves two "slots" left in the place value chart.

H	T	O	t	h	th
		3	. 9	1	5

H	T	O	t	h	th
3	9	1	. 5		

This is identical to thinking that the decimal point moves two steps to the right.

Review: Divide Decimals by Decimals

1. Solve, thinking carefully about how many times the divisor "fits into" the dividend.

   Compare the problems within the same box. What do you notice?

a. $120 \div 20 =$	**e.** $28 \div 4 =$
b. $12 \div 2 =$	**f.** $2.8 \div 0.4 =$
c. $1.2 \div 0.2 =$	**g.** $0.28 \div 0.04 =$
d. $0.12 \div 0.02 =$	**h.** $0.028 \div 0.004 =$

An important principle

Consider any division problem. If you *multiply the dividend and the divisor by the same number*, the **quotient** stays the same. The divisor still "goes into" the dividend as many times as before!

We can use this principle to transform each decimal division problem, such as $3.439 \div 5.6$, into a problem with the same answer, but with a **whole-number divisor**. Once you have a whole number as a divisor, you can use long division.

Example 1. Solve $0.6 \div 0.003$.

We multiply both numbers in the problem by 10 until the divisor is a whole number →

3 goes into 600 as many times as 0.003 goes into 0.6!

$0.6 \div 0.003$	(This is the original problem.)
$6 \div 0.03$	(The divisor is not a whole number yet.)
$60 \div 0.3$	(The divisor is not a whole number yet.)
$600 \div 3$	← Now the divisor is a whole number!

The last problem, $600 \div 3$, is easy to solve. The answer is 200. So, the answer to $0.6 \div 0.03$ **is also 200**.

Check by multiplying: $200 \cdot 0.003$ is 200 times 3 thousandths = 600 thousandths = 0.600 = 0.6. It checks.

---

2. In your head, multiply both the dividend and the divisor by 10 repeatedly until you get a new division problem where the divisor is a whole number. Then divide.

a. $0.8 \div 0.02$	**b.** $12 \div 0.4$	**c.** $4.5 \div 0.05$
_____ ÷ _____	_____ ÷ _____ = _____	_____ ÷ _____
_____ ÷ _____ = _____		_____ ÷ _____ = _____

3. In your head, multiply both the dividend and the divisor by 10, 100, or 1,000 to make a new division problem where the divisor is a whole number. Then divide.

a. $1.6 \div 0.04$	**b.** $2.6 \div 0.2$	**c.** $36 \div 0.009$
_____ ÷ _____ = _____	_____ ÷ _____ = _____	_____ ÷ _____ = _____
d. $0.6 \div 0.003$	**e.** $5.4 \div 0.009$	**f.** $0.5 \div 0.005$
_____ ÷ _____ = _____	_____ ÷ _____ = _____	_____ ÷ _____ = _____

You have already seen this principle with **equivalent fractions**. We can multiply the numerator and the denominator by the same number, and the value of the fraction stays the same!

A fraction is simply a division. Therefore, that same principle that works with fractions also works with division problems: <u>multiply both the dividend and the divisor by the same number</u>, and the value of the whole quotient (answer) does not change.

$$\frac{3}{7} = \frac{21}{49} \qquad \frac{6.4}{0.008} = \frac{6,400}{8} = 800$$

With decimal division, our goal is to make the **divisor into a whole number**. Why? So we can use long division or divide easily using mental math. (If you are using a calculator, there is no need for these changes.)

4. Multiply both the dividend and the divisor by the same given number. Then divide in your head.

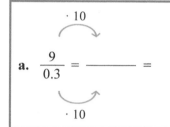

a. $\dfrac{9}{0.3} =$ —— $=$

b. $\dfrac{2}{0.05} =$ —— $=$

c. $\dfrac{0.3}{0.006} =$ —— $=$

5. Do the same as above. Choose a factor that will turn the divisor on the bottom into a whole number. Multiply both the dividend and the divisor by that same factor. Then divide in your head.

a. $\dfrac{3.4}{0.002} =$ —— $=$

b. $\dfrac{0.56}{0.0008} =$ —— $=$

c. $\dfrac{0.15}{0.0003} =$ —— $=$

6. Choose the expressions that have the value 0.2.

a. $\dfrac{2}{10}$
b. $\dfrac{20}{10}$
c. $\dfrac{20}{100}$
d. $\dfrac{20}{1,000}$
e. $\dfrac{200}{1,000}$
f. $\dfrac{20,000}{1,000}$
g. $\dfrac{2,000}{1,000}$
h. $\dfrac{200}{100}$

7. Write six division problems that have a decimal divisor and a quotient of 5.

8. Solve the equations.

a. $0.2x = 0.5$	b. $\dfrac{y}{70} = 0.03$	c. $1.2z = 600$

Example 2. Solve $7.935 \div 0.15$.

We multiply both numbers in the problem by 100, and then the divisor is a whole number. →

$7.935 \div 0.15$ (Multiply both by 100.)

$793.5 \div 15$ ← Now the divisor is a whole number!

We take the last problem, $793.5 \div 15$, and solve it with long division. →
Notice that the *dividend* does not have to be a whole number!

The answer is 52.9. So, the answer to the original problem, $7.935 \div 0.15$, is also 52.9. Check by multiplying (using the *original* problem):

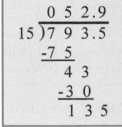

```
    1 4
    5 2.9    ← one decimal digit
  ·  0.1 5   ← two decimal digits
  ─────────
    2 6 4 5
  + 5 2 9 0
  ─────────
    7.9 3 5  ← three decimal digits
```

9. Multiply both the dividend and the divisor by the same number (10, 100, or 1,000) so that you get a divisor that is a *whole number*. Then divide using long division.

a. $27.6 \div 0.3$	b. $2.088 \div 0.06$
c. $5.634 \div 0.9$	d. $1.064 \div 0.008$

Divide Decimals by Decimals 2

A shortcut for dividing decimals by decimals

You have learned to multiply both the dividend and the divisor by a power of ten so that the divisor becomes a whole number.

The shortcut for this is simply *to move the decimal point in both the dividend and the divisor* enough decimal places so that the divisor becomes a whole number.

$$\cdot\ 10$$

$$\frac{5.6}{0.2} = \frac{56}{2} = 28$$

$$\cdot\ 10$$

Move the decimal point in both the dividend and the divisor <u>one step</u> to the right.

$$\cdot\ 1{,}000$$

$$\frac{0.0932}{0.013} = \frac{93.2}{13} \approx 7.17$$

$$\cdot\ 1{,}000$$

Move the decimal point in both the dividend and the divisor <u>three steps</u> to the right.

1. Write an equivalent division problem where the divisor is a whole number. Then solve with long division.

a. $\dfrac{57.2}{0.04}$

b. $\dfrac{23.88}{0.006}$

2. Solve the equations.

a. $0.5x = 7.35$

b. $0.07x = 32.144$

Example. Solve $5.629 \div 0.07$ to two decimal digits.

We multiply both numbers in the problem by 100, and get $562.9 \div 7$.

To solve this to two decimal digits, we need to continue the long division until we have *three* decimal digits; so, we need to write the dividend 562.9 as 562.900.

The answer, to two decimal digits, is 80.41.

To check, multiply 80.41 by the original divisor, 0.07. Because of the rounding, you will not get exactly 5.629, but 5.6287, which is very close. So it checks out correctly.

```
        8 0.4 1 4
   7 )5 6 2.9 0,0
     -5 6
        0 2
       -  0
          2 9
        - 2 8
            1,0
           -  7
              3 0
            - 2 8
                2
```

3. Divide. Use long division and a notebook. If the division is not even, give your answer to <u>two</u> decimal digits.

a. $168.21 \div 0.2$	**b.** $7.2028 \div 0.0026$
c. $98 \div 0.05$	**d.** $47.75 \div 0.018$

4. Mark purchased 2.7 lb of a trail mix that costs $5.50 per pound. He then divided the cost equally with two of his friends. How much was each person's share?

5. Find the value of the expression $\dfrac{2}{b}$ when $b = 0.8$.

Give your answer as a mixed number and as a decimal.

6. Write an expression for each situation.

   a. The cost of n kilograms of nuts that cost p dollars per kilogram.

   b. One-tenth of the cost in (a).

   c. (Challenge) The cost in (a) discounted by 1/10 of the cost.

Puzzle Corner

As long as we multiply or divide both the numerator and denominator by the same number, the quotient remains the same. The number that we use isn't limited to a power of ten. It could be any number.

Annie used this principle to calculate $235 \div 5$ in her head:	Follow the same idea—or come up with one of your own—and find a way to calculate the following divisions *without* a calculator or long division.
$\overset{\cdot\,2}{\curvearrowright}$ $\dfrac{235}{5} = \dfrac{470}{10} = 47$ $\underset{\cdot\,2}{\curvearrowleft}$	**a.** $732 \div 5$ **b.** $842 \div 50$ **c.** $6{,}050 \div 25$ **d.** $250 \div 4$

Convert Customary Measuring Units

Units of length	Units of weight	Units of volume
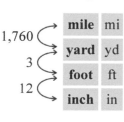 1 mile = 5,280 feet	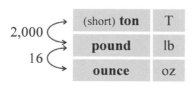	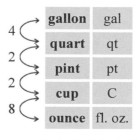

When you convert between units, you either <u>multiply</u> or <u>divide</u> by the conversion factor. But which?

Think whether you need *more* or *fewer* of the units that you will end with. That will tell you whether to multiply or divide by the conversion factor.

Example 1. Let's say you are converting 1,200 feet into <u>miles</u>. Would you expect the amount in miles to be MORE or LESS than 1,200 miles? Surely less, right? The conversion factor is 5,280. You will need to divide 1,200 by 5,280, *not* multiply. We get $1,200 \div 5,280 = 0.227272... \approx 0.23$ miles.

Example 2. Convert 11 ounces to pounds.

Ounces are smaller units than pounds, which means that we need to end up with less than 11 pounds. So, we have to divide by the conversion factor 16. We get $11 \div 16 = 0.6875$ lb ≈ 0.69 lb.

Instead of a decimal, you could give this answer as a fraction very simply: 11 oz $= \dfrac{11}{16}$ lb.

Example 3. Convert 56,000 inches to miles.

Miles are a lot bigger than inches, so we expect to end up with fewer of them. In other words, we expect the number 56,000 to get *smaller* when converting 56,000 inches to miles.

You can convert from inches to miles in two steps: first from inches to feet (conversion factor 12), then from feet to miles (conversion factor 5,280). To get towards a smaller number, we divide:

$56,000 \div 12 \div 5,280 = 0.88383838...$ So 56,000 inches ≈ 0.88 miles.

1. Which conversion is correct—the upper or the lower?

a. 2.46 gal $= 2.46 \times 4$ qt $= 9.84$ qt 2.46 gal $= \dfrac{2.46}{4}$ qt $= 0.615$ qt	**b.** 11 oz $= 11 \times 16$ lb $= 176$ lb 11 oz $= \dfrac{11}{16}$ lb $= 0.6875$ lb
c. 450 ft $= 450 \times 5,280$ mi $= 2,376,000$ mi 450 ft $= \dfrac{450}{5,280}$ mi ≈ 0.085 mi	**d.** 12.6 ft $= 12.6 \times 12$ in $= 151.2$ in 12.6 ft $= \dfrac{12.6}{12}$ in $= 1.05$ in

2. Convert to the given unit. Round your answers to two decimals, if needed.

a. 564 ft = _____ mi	**c.** 3,400 yd = _____ mi	**e.** 0.28 mi = _____ ft
b. 45,000 ft = _____ mi	**d.** 7.8 mi = _____ ft	**f.** 10.17 mi = _____ yd

3. Convert to the given unit. Round your answers to two decimals, if needed.

a. 3 in = _____ ft	**c.** 14.7 ft = _____ in	**e.** 281 in = _____ ft
b. 21 in = _____ ft	**d.** 0.8 ft = _____ in	**f.** 7 1/3 ft = _____ in

4. Convert to the given unit. Round your answers to two decimals, if needed.

a. 5 oz = _____ lb	**c.** 3.6 lb = _____ oz	**e.** 127 oz = _____ lb
b. 35 oz = _____ lb	**d.** 0.391 lb = _____ oz	**f.** 6 3/4 lb = _____ oz

5. Convert to the given unit. Round your answers to two decimals, if needed.

a. 6.4 gal = _____ qt	**d.** 0.56 qt = _____ fl. oz.	**g.** 0.054 T = _____ lb
b. 78 fl. oz. = _____ qt	**e.** 560 qt = _____ gal	**h.** 1,200 lb = _____ T
c. 2.3 qt = _____ fl. oz.	**f.** 3.2 T = _____ lb	**i.** 6,750 lb = _____ T

Example 4. Convert 6 lb 15 oz into ounces.

Simply change the 6 lb into ounces first, then add the 15 ounces.

Example 5. Convert 372 ounces into pounds and ounces.

For the pounds, figure out how many 16-ounce increments there are in 372. That is done by dividing 372 ÷ 16. If you use long division, you will have a remainder, and the remainder tells you the individual ounces that are "left over." If you use a calculator, you will get a decimal number: 372 ÷ 16 = 23.25. The whole pounds are 23.

For the ounces, you can take the decimal part, 0.25, and figure out how many ounces 0.25 lb is. Another way is to calculate 23 × 16 = 368, and since that is 4 less than 372, there are four ounces.

In summary, 372 oz = 23 lb 4 oz.

---

6. Convert to the given unit. Round your answers to two decimals, if needed.

a. 2 ft 6 in = _____ in	**c.** 162 in = _____ ft _____ in	**e.** 254 in = _____ ft _____ in
b. 7 ft 11 in = _____ in	**d.** 79 in = _____ ft _____ in	**f.** 1,028 in = _____ ft _____ in

7. Convert to the given unit. Round your answers to two decimals, if needed.

a. 6 lb 9 oz = _____ oz	**c.** 86 oz = _____ lb _____ oz	**e.** 483 oz = _____ lb _____ oz
b. 11 lb 12 oz = _____ oz	**d.** 145 oz = _____ lb _____ oz	**f.** 591 oz = _____ lb _____ oz

Example 6. Convert 2.45 pounds to pounds and ounces.

This time, the 2 from 2.45 gives us the pounds. But the ounces? We need to convert the decimal part, 0.45 pounds, into ounces.

One pound is 16 ounces. Therefore, 0.45 pounds is $0.45 \times 16 = 7.2$ ounces. Most of the time, we give weights using whole pounds and whole ounces, so this would be rounded to 7 ounces. So, 2.45 lb is about 2 lb 7 oz.

8. Convert to the given unit. Round your answers to whole inches and whole ounces.

a. 2.7 ft = ____ ft _____ in	**c.** 3.15 ft = ____ ft _____ in	**e.** 55.46 lb = ____ lb _____ oz
b. 10.2 ft = ____ ft _____ in	**d.** 7.8 lb = ____ lb _____ oz	**f.** 8.204 lb = ____ lb _____ oz

With the worksheet maker at https://www.homeschoolmath.net/worksheets/measuring.php you can make more conversion problems between measuring units for extra practice.

9. You can add, subtract, and even multiply customary measuring units in columns.

a.	b.	c.
5 lb 14 oz + 7 lb 13 oz	34 ft 6 in 62 ft 9 in + 11 ft 11 in	6 qt 24 oz 1 qt 7 oz 4 qt 18 oz + 2 qt 13 oz
d.	e.	f.
60 ft 2 in − 14 ft 8 in	2 lb 7 oz × 5	5 h 34 min − 2 h 45 min

10. Right now Jack is 4 feet 3 inches tall. He has been growing steadily at the rate of 2 3/8 inches per year for three years. How tall was he three years ago?

11. How many 21-inch wide chairs can you put in a row in a room that is 40 ft wide?

What if you wish to leave two 3-foot aisles?

12. Jack made 4 quarts of peppermint tea. He wants to serve it in small glasses in 6-ounce servings. How many glasses does he need?

13. You are packing math books that weigh 2 lb 3 oz each into a box that must not weigh more than 60 pounds. How many books can you put into the box?

14. Find the better deal.

   a. A 13-oz bottle of shampoo for $5.69 or a 1-quart bottle of shampoo for $13.99.

   b. 12 oz of potatoes for $0.35 or 8 lb of potatoes for $4.10

15. A bottle of olive oil contains 25.5 oz and costs $4.84. What is the price per quart?

16. **a.** A gallon of ice cream is divided evenly among 17 people. How much does each person get (in ounces)?

   b. Your ice cream scoop holds 1.5 oz. How many scoops do you need to give each person so everyone gets an equal share?

17. You bought 10 pounds of strawberries and divided them evenly among seven people. How much did each person get (in pounds and ounces)?

Convert Metric Measuring Units

The metric system has one basic unit for each thing we might measure: For length, the unit is the **meter**. For weight, it is the **gram**. And for volume, it is the **liter**.

All of the other units for measuring length, weight, or volume are *derived* from the basic units using *prefixes*. The prefixes tell us what multiple of the basic unit the *derived unit* is.

For example, centiliter is 1/100 part of a liter (*centi* means 1/100).

Prefix	Abbreviated	Meaning
kilo-	k	1,000
hecto-	h	100
deka-	da	10
-	-	(the basic unit)
deci-	d	1/10
centi-	c	1/100
milli-	m	1/1,000

Unit	Abbr	Meaning
kilometer	km	1,000 meters
hectometer	hm	100 meters
decameter	dam	10 meters
meter	m	(the basic unit)
decimeter	dm	1/10 meter
centimeter	cm	1/100 meter
millimeter	mm	1/1,000 meter

Unit	Abbr	Meaning
kilogram	kg	1,000 grams
hectogram	hg	100 grams
dekagram	dag	10 grams
gram	g	(the basic unit)
decigram	dg	1/10 gram
centigram	cg	1/100 gram
milligram	mg	1/1,000 gram

Unit	Abbr	Meaning
kiloliter	kl	1,000 liters
hectoliter	hl	100 liters
dekaliter	dal	10 liters
liter	L	(the basic unit)
deciliter	dl	1/10 liter
centiliter	cl	1/100 liter
milliliter	ml	1/1,000 liter

1. Write these amounts using the basic units (meters, grams, or liters) by "translating" the prefixes. Use both fractions and decimals, like this: 3 cm = 3/100 m = 0.03 m (since "centi" means "hundredth part").

a. 3 cm   =   *3/100 m*   =   *0.03 m*

  5 mm   = _____ m   = _____ m

  7 dl   = _____ L   = _____ L

b. 2 cg   = _____ g   = _____ g

  6 ml   = _____ L   = _____ L

  1 dg   = _____ g   = _____ g

2. Write the amounts in basic units (meters, grams, or liters) by "translating" the prefixes.

a. 3 kl   = _____ L

  8 dag   = _____ g

  6 hm   = _____ m

b. 2 dam   = _____ m

  9 hl   = _____ L

  7 kg   = _____ g

c. 70 km   = _____ m

  5 hg   = _____ g

  8 dal   = _____ L

3. Write the amounts with derived units (units with prefixes) and a single-digit number.

a. 3,000 g = __3__ __kg__

  800 L = __8__ _____

  60 m = __6__ _____

b. 0.01 m = _____ _____

  0.2 L = _____ _____

  0.005 g = _____ _____

c. 0.04 L = _____ _____

  0.8 m = _____ _____

  0.007 L = _____ _____

4. Write using prefixed units.

    a. 0.04 meters = 4 cm   **b.** 0.005 grams = 5 _____   **c.** 0.037 meters = 37 _____

    d. 400 liters = 4 _____   **e.** 0.6 meters = 6 _____   **f.** 2,000 meters = 2 _____

    g. 0.206 liters = 206 _____   **h.** 20 meters = 2 _____   **i.** 0.9 grams = 9 _____

5. Change into the basic unit (either meter, liter, or gram). Think of the meaning of the prefix.

    a. 45 cm = *0.45 m*   **b.** 65 mg =   **c.** 2 dm =

    d. 81 km =   **e.** 6 ml =   **f.** 758 mg =

    g. 2 kl =   **h.** 8 dl =   **i.** 9 dag =

Example 1. Convert 2.5 cg to grams.

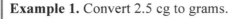

					2.	5
kg	hg	dag	g	dg	cg	mg

→

			0.	0	2	5
kg	hg	dag	g	dg	cg	mg

Write 2.5 in the chart so that "2", which is in the ones place, is placed in the centigrams place.

Move the decimal point just after the grams place. Add necessary zeros. Answer: 0.025 g.

---

6. Write the measurements in the place value charts.

    a. 12.3 m

km	hm	dam	m	dm	cm	mm

    c. 56 cl

kl	hl	dal	l	dl	cl	ml

    b. 78 mm

km	hm	dam	m	dm	cm	mm

    d. 9.83 hg

kg	hg	dag	g	dg	cg	mg

7. Convert the measurements to the given units, using the charts above.

	m	dm	cm	mm
a. 12.3 m	12.3			
b. 78 mm				78 mm
	L	**dl**	**cl**	**ml**
c. 56 cl				
	g	**dg**	**cg**	**mg**
d. 9.83 hg				

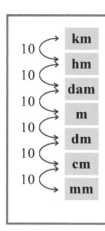

You can also convert measurements by thinking of how many steps apart the two units are in the chart and then multiplying or dividing by the corresponding power of ten.

Example 2. Convert 2.4 km into centimeters.

There are five steps from kilometers to centimeters. That means we would multiply 2.4 by 10, five times—or multiply 2.4 by 10^5.

$2.4 \cdot 100{,}000 = 240{,}000$, so 2.4 km = 240,000 cm.

Example 3. Convert 2,900 cg into hectograms.

"Centi" and "hecto" are four steps apart, so we will divide by $10^4 = 10{,}000$.
$2{,}900 \div 10{,}000 = 0.29$, so 2,900 cg = 0.29 hg.

8. Convert the measurements. You can write the numbers in the place value charts or count the steps.

a. 560 cl = _____ L

b. 0.493 kg = _____ dag

c. 24.5 hm = _____ cm

d. 491 cm = _____ m

e. 35,200 mg = _____ g

f. 32 dal = _____ cl

g. 0.483 km = _____ dm

h. 0.0056 km = _____ cm

i. 1.98 hl = _____ dl

j. 9.5 dl = _____ L

kl	hl	dal	l	dl	cl	ml

kg	hg	dag	g	dg	cg	mg

km	hm	dam	m	dm	cm	mm

9. Each measurement has an error, either in the unit or in the decimal point. Correct them.

a. The length of a pencil: 13 m

b. The length of an eraser: 45 cm

c. Circumference of Dad's waist: 9.2 m

d. The height of a room: 0.24 m

e. Jack's height: 1.70 mm

f. Jenny's height: 1.34 cm

10. Find the total …

a. … weight of books that weigh individually:
1.2 kg, 1.04 kg, 520 g, and 128 g.

b. … volume of containers whose individual volumes are:
1.4 L, 2.25 L, 550 ml, 240 ml, and 4 dl.

11. A dropper measures 4 ml. How many full droppers can you get from a 2-dl bottle?

12. Once a day, a nurse has to give a patient 3 mg of medicine for each kilogram of body weight. The patient weighs 70 kg. How many days will it take for the patient to take 2 g of medicine?

Convert Between Customary and Metric

EASY ballpark figures:	Good to remember also:	Exact figures:	
1 m ≈ 1 yd	1 in ≈ 2.5 cm	1 inch = 2.54 cm	1 quart = 0.946 L
1 L ≈ 1 qt	1 mi ≈ 1.6 km (4 laps on a 400-m track)	1 foot = 0.3048 m	1 ounce = 28.35 g
1 kg ≈ 2 lb		1 yard = 0.9144 m	1 lb = 0.454 kg
	1 oz ≈ 30 g	1 mile = 1.6093 km	1 kg = 2.2 lb

Example 1. Convert 17 inches to centimeters.

The table lists 1 inch as 2.54 cm. Therefore, 17 inches is simply 17 times that, or 17 × 2.54 cm = 43.18 cm.

Example 2. Convert 650 grams to ounces.

The table does *not* list 1 gram as so many ounces. If it did, we would multiply. Instead, it says that **1 ounce = 28.35 g**. So, each 28.35 grams makes one ounce. We *divide* to find how many times 28.35 grams fits into 650 grams—and that is the amount of ounces.

650 g ÷ 28.35 g/oz ≈ 22.93 oz or about 23 oz.

You can also see the need for dividing once you notice that ounces are bigger units than grams (1 ounce is about 28 grams). We need *fewer* of a bigger unit. Therefore, the number in 650 grams must get a lot smaller when it is converted into ounces.

In each conversion, you either <u>multiply</u> or <u>divide</u> by the conversion factor.

For example, the table gives 1 yard = 0.9144 m. If you have to convert yards into meters, multiply by 0.9144. To convert meters into yards, divide.

1. Circle the conversion on the right that is closest in size to the given measurement on the left.

a. 1 inch	1 cm 2.5 cm 5 cm	**b.** 1 foot	5 cm 10 cm 30 cm	**c.** 1 mile	1.5 km 2.5 km 3.5 km	**d.** 1 qt	1 L 100 ml 2.5 L
e. 2 kg	2 lb 4 lb 6 lb	**f.** 1 m	12 in 3 ft 3 yd	**g.** 1 cup	5 ml 30 ml 240 ml	**h.** 1 gal	4 L 6 L 8 L

2. Which is more? (Write <, =, or > between the measurements.)

a. 1 cm 1 in	**b.** 1 L 1 qt	**c.** 1 kg 1 lb	**d.** 1 g 1 oz
e. 4 in 20 cm	**f.** 5 kg 20 lb	**g.** 3 gal 2 L	**h.** 7 m 4 ft

3. Convert between the units. Use a calculator when needed. Round your answers to two decimals.

a.	b.	c.	d.
1 cm = _____ in	1 m = _____ yd	2 L = _____ qt	5 kg = _____ lb
25 cm = _____ in	5.4 m = _____ ft	4.6 L = _____ qt	0.568 kg = _____ lb

e.	f.	g.	h.
5 in = _____ cm	30 ft = _____ m	1 gal = _____ L	75 lb = _____ kg
10 in = _____ cm	22 ft = _____ m	3 1/2 qt = _____ L	8.5 lb = _____ kg

4. In the U.S., a common speed limit is 55 miles per hour.
   This corresponds most closely to a European speed limit of:
   (a) 70 km/h   (b) 80 km/h   (c) 90 km/h   (d) 100 km/h

5. Which is a better deal, a 24-ounce bottle of honey for $6.75
   or a 1-liter bottle of honey for $9.25?
   Hint: For both bottles, find either the price per ounce or the price per liter.
   Note that here the term "ounces" refers to fluid ounces of volume,
   rather than ounces of weight.

6. On the label of a food container, you can often find
   its capacity. A container's label reads 64 oz.

   a. Is it bigger than one that is 2.2 L?

   b. If so, how much larger? If not, how much smaller?

7. Angela weighs 56 kg, Theresa weighs 128 lb, Judy
   weighs 137 lb, and Elizabeth weighs 60 kg.
   List the girls in order from the lightest to the heaviest.

8. One marathon is 26.21875 miles.
   How long in kilometers is a half marathon?

Chapter 3 Mixed Review

1. Which power of ten is equal to a hundred million? (Powers and Exponents/Ch.1)

2. Write in expanded form using exponents. (Powers and Exponents/Ch.1)

    350,0480

3. Estimate the result using mental math and rounded numbers. Find the exact value using a calculator. Also, find the error of estimation. (Rounding and Estimating/Ch.1)

a. 213 · 5,829	**b.** 435,212 ÷ 993
Estimation:	Estimation:
Exact value:	Exact value:
Error of estimation:	Error of estimation:

4. Eric bought two printers. One cost $98 and the other cost 6/7 of that price. (Lessons in Problem Solving/Ch.1) Find the total cost.

5. Two students measured the marked angle of this triangle: (Fifth grade concepts)

    One of them got 38° and another got 142°. Then a third student said, "A triangle cannot have an obtuse angle like what you measured. So, 142° cannot be right, and 38° is right."

    What do you think about this student's reasoning? Is it correct?

    Why or why not?

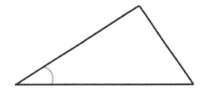

6. Find the inside volume of this cabin, in cubic *meters*. (Fifth grade concepts)

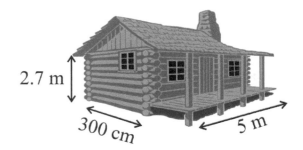

2.7 m

300 cm

5 m

7. **Write an expression.** (Words and Expressions/Ch.2)

    a. the quantity $t - 1$ squared   **b.** x less than 9

    c. 7 more than S **d.** 8 times the sum of 4, x and 2

    e. the quotient of x^2 and the quantity $x + 1$

8. **Evaluate the expressions for the given value of the variable.** (Expressions, Part 1/Ch.2)

a. $3x - 11$ when $x = 8$	**b.** $\dfrac{3}{z} \cdot 7$ when $z = 5$
c. $t + \dfrac{2t}{5}$, when $t = 10$	**d.** $\dfrac{a + 10}{a - 9}$, when a is 12

9. **Simplify the expressions.** (Writing and Simplifying Expressions 1/Ch.2)

a. $x \cdot x \cdot x \cdot x \cdot x$	**b.** $p + 2 + p$
c. $5 \cdot x \cdot x \cdot 2 \cdot x$	**d.** $9z - 2z + z$
e. $f + f + x + x + f$	**f.** $6 + s + 2s + 4$

10. **Write an inequality for each phrase. Choose a variable to represent the quantity in question.** (Inequalities/Ch.2)

    a. The AC runs at least 18 hours per day.

    b. The jacket can cost a maximum of $40.

    c. She is over 12 years old.

11. **Solve the inequality** $x + 1 < 8$ **in the set** $\{3, 4, 5, 6, 7, 8\}$.
(Inequalities/Ch.2)

12. **Multiply using the distributive property.** (The Distributive Property/Ch.2)

a. $3(5x + 6) =$	**b.** $2(8x + 2 + y) =$

13. **Solve the equations.** (More Equations/Ch.2)

a. $\quad x + 78 \;=\; 412$ $\quad\quad=$ $\quad\quad=$	**b.** $\quad \dfrac{x}{9} \;=\; 600$ $\quad\quad=$ $\quad\quad=$	**c.** $\quad y - 5 \;=\; 12 + 18$ $\quad\quad=$ $\quad\quad=$

Chapter 3 Review

1. Write as decimals.

   a. three ten-thousandths

   b. 39,234 hundred-thousandths

   c. 4 millionths

   d. 2 and 5 thousandths

2. Write as fractions.

   a. 0.00039

   b. 0.0391

   c. 4.0032

3. Write as decimals.

a. $\dfrac{3}{4}$	**b.** $1\dfrac{2}{5}$	**c.** $\dfrac{17}{20}$	**d.** $\dfrac{11}{25}$

4. Fill in the table, noting that 1 micrometer is 1 millionth of a meter ($\dfrac{1}{1,000,000}$ of a meter).

Organism	Size (fraction)	Size (micrometers)	Size (decimal)
amoeba proteus	$\dfrac{600}{1,000,000}$ meters	_____ micrometers	0.0006 m
protozoa	from $\dfrac{10}{1,000,000}$ to $\dfrac{50}{1,000,000}$ m	from __10__ to __50__ micrometers	from _____ to _____ m
bacteria	from $\dfrac{1}{1,000,000}$ to $\dfrac{5}{1,000,000}$ m	from _____ to _____ micrometers	from _____ to _____ m

5. Write in order from the smallest to the largest.

a. 0.0256 0.000526 0.0062	**b.** 0.000087 0.000007 0.00008

6. Round to...

	0.37182	0.04828384	0.39627	0.099568
the nearest hundredth				
the nearest ten-thousandth				

7. Calculate in your head.

a. $0.02 + \dfrac{4}{1,000}$	**b.** $0.7 + \dfrac{5}{100}$	**c.** $3.021 + \dfrac{22}{1,000}$

8. Calculate. Remember to line up the decimal points.

    a. $2.1 - 1.09342$

    b. $17 + 93.1 + 0.0483$

9. Find the value of the expression $y + 0.04$ when

a. $y = 0.1$	**b.** $y = 0.01$	**c.** $y = 0.0001$

10. Divide in your head. For each division, write a corresponding multiplication.

a. $0.48 \div 6 =$	**b.** $1.5 \div 0.3 =$	**c.** $0.056 \div 0.008 =$

11. Multiply in your head.

a. $3 \cdot 0.006 =$	**b.** $0.2 \cdot 0.6 =$	**c.** $0.9 \cdot 0.0007 =$

12. Now, $327 \cdot 4$ is $1\,308$. Based on that, figure out the answer to $32.7 \cdot 0.004$.

13. **a.** Estimate the answer to $8.9 \cdot 0.061$.

    b. Calculate the exact answer.

14. Solve the equations by thinking logically.

a. $3 \cdot$ _____ $= 0.09$	**b.** $0.2 \cdot$ _____ $= 0.024$	**c.** $0.03 \cdot$ _____ $= 0.0015$

15. Solve the equations. If necessary, round your answers to three decimals.

a. $0.4p = 90$	**b.** $0.03x = 5.2$	**c.** $y + 0.056 = 0.38$

16. Jim cut seven 0.56-meter pieces out of a 4-meter board.
    How much is left?

17. Multiply or divide the decimals by the powers of ten.

a. $10^6 \cdot 21.7 =$	**b.** $100 \cdot 0.00456 =$
c. $2.3912 \div 1,000 =$	**d.** $324 \div 10^5 =$
e. $10^5 \cdot 0.003938 =$	**f.** $0.7 \div 10^4 =$

18. Find the value of the expression $\dfrac{a}{b} + 1$
    when $a = 2.068$ and $b = 0.8$.

19. Divide, giving your answer as a decimal. If necessary, round the answers to three decimal digits.

a. $28.2 \div 2$	**b.** $0.11 \div 15$
c. $\dfrac{4}{9}$	**d.** $\dfrac{5}{11}$

20. Fill in the entries missing from this table.

Prefix	Meaning	Units - length	Units - mass	Units - volume
			centigram (cg)	
deci-				deciliter (dl)
	ten = 10		decagram (dag)	
				hectoliter (hl)

21. Change into the basic unit (meter, liter, or gram). Think of the meaning of the prefix.

    a. 34 dl   **b.** 89 cg   **c.** 16 kl

22. Convert the measurements into the given units.

    a. 2.7 L = _____ dl = _____ cl = _____ ml

    b. 5,600 m = _____ km = _____ dm = _____ cm

    c. 676 g = _____ dg = _____ cg = _____ mg

23. You have eleven empty soda bottles. Six are 350 ml, two are 2 liters and three are 9 dl. What is the total amount of water that you can put into them?

24. Convert into the given units. Round your answers to 2 decimals if needed.

a. 56 m = _____ km	**c.** 2.7 L = _____ ml	**e.** 0.48 km = _____ m
b. 134 g = _____ kg	**d.** 0.391 kg = _____ g	**f.** 2.45 m = _____ m _____ cm

25. For a parade, each of 230 children needs a ribbon that is at least 60 cm long. If you buy a 150-m roll of ribbon, how long will the ribbons be if you divide the roll equally?

26. A scientist measured the length of some tadpoles caught from a pond. The recorded lengths are below, in centimeters. Find the average length of the tadpoles.
3.2   3.1   3.4   3.1   3.5   2.9   2.7   2.7   3.0   3.0   3.1
3.4   3.2   2.8   2.8   2.9   3.6   3.4   2.9   3.4   3.1

Chapter 4: Ratios
Introduction

In this chapter we concentrate on the concept of ratio and various applications involving ratios and rates.

The chapter starts out with the basic concepts of ratio, rate and unit rate. We also connect the concept of rates (specifically, tables of equivalent rates) with ordered pairs, use equations (such as $y = 3x$) to describe these tables, and plot the ordered pairs in the coordinate plane.

Next, we study various kinds of word problems involving ratios and use a bar model to solve these problems in two separate lessons. These lessons tie ratios in with the student's previous knowledge of bar models as a tool for problem solving.

Lastly, students encounter the concept of aspect ratio, which is simply the ratio of a rectangle's width to its height or length, and they solve a variety of problems involving aspect ratio.

This chapter contains lots of opportunities for problem solving, once again. In the lessons that use bar models, encourage your student(s) to communicate their thinking and explain (justify) how they solved the problems. It doesn't have to be fancy. All we are looking for is some explanation of what the student did and why. The bar models provide an excellent way for the students to demonstrate their reasoning here. Essentially, they are practicing constructing a **mathematical argument**.

Once again, there are some free videos for the topics of this chapter at **https://www.mathmammoth.com/videos/** (choose 6th grade).

The Lessons in Chapter 4

	page	span
Ratios and Rates	145	*4 pages*
Unit Rates	149	*2 pages*
Using Equivalent Rates	151	*4 pages*
Ratio Problems and Bar Models 1	155	*3 pages*
Ratio Problems and Bar Models 2	158	*3 pages*
Aspect Ratio	161	*2 pages*
Using Ratios to Convert Measuring Units	163	*4 pages*
Chapter 4 Mixed Review	167	*2 pages*
Chapter 4 Review	169	*2 pages*

Helpful Resources on the Internet

We have compiled a list of Internet resources that match the topics in this chapter. This list of links includes web pages that offer:

- **online practice** for concepts;

- online **games**, or occasionally, printable games;

- **animations** and interactive **illustrations** of math concepts;

- **articles** that teach a math concept.

We heartily recommend you take a look at the list. Many of our customers love using these resources to supplement the bookwork. You can use the resources as you see fit for extra practice, to illustrate a concept better and even just for some fun. Enjoy!

https://l.mathmammoth.com/gr6ch4

SCAN ME

Ratios and Rates

A **ratio** is simply a *comparison* of two numbers or other quantities.

To compare the circles to the triangles in the picture, we say that the *ratio of circles to triangles* is 5:4 (read "five to four").

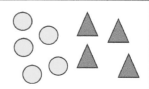

We can write this ratio (in text) in many different ways:

- The ratio of circles to triangles is 5:4 (read "5 to 4").
- The ratio of circles to triangles is 5 to 4.
- The ratio of circles to triangles is $\frac{5}{4}$.
- For each five circles, there are four triangles.

The two numbers in the ratio are called the **first term** and the **second term** of the ratio.

In this picture, the ratio of males to females is 4:3. However, the ratio of *females to males* is **3:4**. The order in which the terms are mentioned does matter!

We can also compare a part to the whole. The ratio of males to everyone is 4:7.

Also, we can use fractions to describe the same image: $\frac{4}{7}$ of the people are males, and $\frac{3}{7}$ are females.

1. Describe the images using ratios and fractions.

a.

The ratio of circles to pentagons is _____ : _____

The ratio of pentagons to all shapes is _____ : _____

 of the shapes are pentagons.

b.

The ratio of hearts to stars is _____ : _____

The ratio of stars to all shapes is _____ : _____

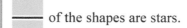 of the shapes are stars.

2. **a.** Draw a picture: There are hearts and circles, and the ratio of hearts to all the shapes is 1:3.

   b. What is the ratio of hearts to circles?

3. Look at the picture of the triangles and circles. If we drew more triangles and circles in the same ratio, how many circles would there be …

   a. … for 9 triangles?

   b. … for 15 triangles?

   c. … for 300 triangles?

We can **simplify** ratios in exactly the same way we simplify fractions (using division).

The ratio of circles to triangles is $\frac{6}{2} = \frac{3}{1}$. We say that 6:2 and 3:1 are **equivalent ratios**.

The simplified ratio 3:1 means that for each three circles, there is one triangle.

Example 1. When we simplify the ratio of hearts to stars to the *lowest terms*, we get $\frac{12}{16} = \frac{3}{4}$, or 12:16 = 3:4. This means that for each three hearts, there are four stars.

We could also simplify like this: 12:16 = 6:8. These two ratios are equivalent, but neither is simplified to the lowest terms.

4. Write the ratios, and then simplify them to lowest terms.

    a. The ratio of diamonds to triangles is _____ : _____ or _____ : _____ .

       There are _____ diamonds to every _____ triangles.

    b. The ratio of pentagons to circles is _____ : _____

       or _____ : _____ .

       There are _____ circles to every _____ pentagons.

5. **a.** Draw a picture in which (1) there are five squares for each two hearts, and (2) there is a total of six hearts.

    b. Write the ratio of all hearts to all squares, and simplify this ratio to lowest terms.

    c. Write the ratio of all shapes to hearts, and simplify this to lowest terms.

6. Write the ratios using a colon. Simplify the ratios if possible.

    a. 15 to 20   **b.** 16 to 4

    c. 25 to 10   **d.** 13 to 30

7. Write the equivalent ratios. Think about equivalent fractions.

a. $\frac{5}{2} = \frac{20}{}$	**b.** 3 : 4 = 9 : _____	**c.** 16 : 18 = ____ : 9	**d.** $\frac{5}{1}$ $\frac{}{4}$
e. 2 to 100 = 1 to _____		**f.** _____ to 40 = 3 to 5	**g.** 5 : ____ = 1 to 20

We can also form ratios using quantities with units. For example, in the ratio 5 km : 8 km, both terms contain the unit "km". We can then simplify the ratio, canceling the units "km": $\dfrac{5 \text{ km}}{8 \text{ km}} = \dfrac{5}{8}$.

8. Write ratios of the given quantities. Use the fraction line to write the ratios. Then, simplify the ratios. In most of the problems, you will need to *convert* one quantity so it has the same measuring unit as the other.

a. 2 kg and 400 g	**b.** 200 ml and 2 L
$\dfrac{2 \text{ kg}}{400 \text{ g}} = \dfrac{2{,}000 \text{ g}}{400 \text{ g}} = \dfrac{2{,}000}{400} = \dfrac{5}{1}$	
c. 400 ml and 5 L	**d.** 800 m and 1.4 km
e. 120 cm and 1.8 m	**f.** 3 cm 4 mm and 1 cm 4 mm

If the two terms in the ratio have *different* units, then the ratio is also called a **rate**.

Example 2. "5 kilometers to 40 minutes" is a rate. It is comparing the quantities "5 kilometers" and "40 minutes," perhaps for the purpose of giving us the speed at which a person is walking.

We can write this rate as 5 kilometers : 40 minutes or $\dfrac{5 \text{ kilometers}}{40 \text{ minutes}}$ or 5 kilometers *per* 40 minutes.

The word "per" in a rate signifies the same thing as a colon or a fraction line.

This rate can be simplified: $\dfrac{5 \text{ kilometers}}{40 \text{ minutes}} = \dfrac{1 \text{ kilometer}}{8 \text{ minutes}}$. The person walks 1 kilometer in 8 minutes.

Example 3. Simplify the rate "15 pencils per 100¢." Solution: $\dfrac{15 \text{ pencils}}{100¢} = \dfrac{3 \text{ pencils}}{20¢}$.

9. Write each rate using a colon, the word "per," or a fraction line. Then simplify it.

a. Annie walks at a constant speed of 3 kilometers in half an hour.

b. In this county, there are five teachers for every 60 pupils.

c. Each three kilograms of rice costs $4.50.

10. Fill in the missing numbers to form equivalent rates.

| a. $\dfrac{2 \text{ cm}}{30 \text{ min}} = \dfrac{}{15 \text{ min}} = \dfrac{}{45 \text{ min}}$ | b. $\dfrac{\$72}{8 \text{ hr}} = \dfrac{}{1 \text{ hr}} = \dfrac{}{10 \text{ hr}}$ |
| c. $\dfrac{1/4 \text{ km}}{10 \text{ min}} = \dfrac{}{1 \text{ hr}} = \dfrac{}{5 \text{ hr}}$ | d. $\dfrac{\$84.40}{8 \text{ hr}} = \dfrac{}{2 \text{ hr}} = \dfrac{}{10 \text{ hr}}$ |

11. Express these rates in lowest terms.

| a. $44 : 4 hr | b. $30 : 8 kg |
| c. 420 km : 8 hr | d. 16 apples for $12 |

12. The rate of pencils to dollars is constant. Fill in the table.

Pencils	Dollars
1	
2	
3	0.75
6	
7	
8	

13. The rate of kilometers to liters remains constant. Fill in the table.

Kilometers							150	
Liters	1	2	3	4	5	10	15	50

14. An automobile travels at a constant speed of 80 km/hour. This means the *rate* of kilometers to hours remains the same. Fill in the table.

Km	10	20	80	100	150	200	500
Minutes							

15. You can use a table like in the previous problems to solve this problem. Six pairs of scissors cost $21. How much would five pairs cost?

16. You can use a table like in the previous problems to solve this problem. Mark can type at a constant rate 225 words in five minutes. How many words can he type in 12 minutes?

Unit Rates

In a **<u>unit rate</u>**, the second term of the rate is *one* of something, or a unit.

For example, 5 dollars per 1 pound is a unit rate. It is commonly said as "5 dollars per pound," but the "per pound" means "per <u>one</u> pound". See more examples of unit rates:

35 words per (one) minute	$3.70/kg	2/3 cup of sugar per 1 cup of flour
45 miles per hour	each student gets 3 pencils	$0.70 per marker

To change a rate that is not a unit rate into a unit rate, simply <u>divide</u>.

Example 1. To change the rate $16 for 6 cups into a unit rate, divide the numbers (16 divided by 6):

We get: $\dfrac{\$16}{6 \text{ cups}} = \dfrac{\$2.67}{1 \text{ cup}}$, which is more commonly written as $2.67 per cup.

Example 2. Two tablespoons of salt in 5 ounces of water is the unit rate 2/5 tablespoons of salt per 1 ounce of water.

To see that, write it using the fraction line: $\dfrac{2 \text{ tbsp}}{5 \text{ oz}}$ = 2/5 tbsp per oz.

1. Give two examples of unit rates (for example, a unit price and a speed).

2. Change to unit rates.

a. $15 for five cups	**b.** 180 miles in six hours	**c.** 10,000 people and five doctors

3. Change to unit rates. Give the rate using the word "per" or the slash /.

   a. To paint 130 square meters, you need to use 15 liters of paint.

   b. Joanne's Internet speed is 100 megabits in 25 seconds.

   c. Each group of five students gets two calculators.

   d. 7 teaspoons of vanilla for each 4 cups of batter.

   e. We paid $75 for fifteen lunches.

   f. $111 for three mattresses.
    Hint: use long division.

You can often solve problems involving rates by first calculating the unit rate.

If you buy a package of fifteen flashlights that costs $75, how much would you charge your neighbor for two flashlights?

We will find the unit rate—or the price for one—by dividing:

$75 ÷ 15 = $5.00. For two, you would ask $10.00.

4. It took Jack 3 hours to paint 12 meters of fence. Painting at the same speed, how long will it take him to paint the 30 meters of the fence that are left?

5. **a.** If it took Jerry 7 hours to mow 4 lawns of about the same size, then at the same rate, how many lawns of that size could he mow in 35 hours?

   b. What is the unit rate at which Jerry mows lawns?

6. An airplane travels at a constant speed and covers 2,500 miles in five hours. Traveling at the same speed, how far can it travel in eight hours?

7. A recipe has a ratio of 1 1/2 cups of sugar to 4 cups of flour. What is the unit rate of sugar to flour?
   Hint: you will need to use division of mixed numbers.

8. Mary is instructed to apply 11 kg of fertilizer to her lawn that measures 929 m^2. Using the same rate, how much fertilizer should she apply to a lawn that is 650 m^2?

9. Forty-five liters of paint was enough to cover 700 m^2 of a wall. How much of the wall would 6 liters of paint have covered?

Paint							
Wall area							

Using Equivalent Rates

Example 1. If Jake can ride his bike to a town that is 33 kilometers away in 45 minutes, how far can he ride in 1 hour?

Let's form some equivalent rates, starting with 33 kilometers per 45 minutes and hoping to arrive at so many kilometers per 60 minutes.

However, it is not easy to go directly from 45 minutes to 60 minutes (1 hour). So, first you figure the rate for <u>15 minutes</u>, which *is* easy.

Why? Because to get from 45 minutes to 15 minutes you simply divide both terms of the rate by 3.

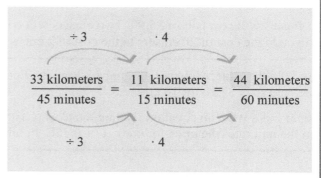

Then from 15 minutes, we can easily get to 60 minutes: Just multiply both terms by 4. We find that he can ride 44 kilometers in one hour.

1. Write the equivalent rates.

a. $\dfrac{15 \text{ km}}{3 \text{ hr}} = \dfrac{}{1 \text{ hr}} = \dfrac{}{15 \text{ min}} = \dfrac{}{45 \text{ min}}$

b. $\dfrac{\$6}{45 \text{ min}} = \dfrac{}{15 \text{ min}} = \dfrac{}{1 \text{ hr}} = \dfrac{}{1 \text{ hr } 45 \text{ min}}$

c. $\dfrac{3 \text{ cm}}{8 \text{ m}} = \dfrac{}{2 \text{ m}} = \dfrac{}{12 \text{ m}} = \dfrac{}{20 \text{ m}}$

d. $\dfrac{115 \text{ words}}{2 \text{ min}} = \dfrac{}{1 \text{ min}} = \dfrac{}{3 \text{ min}}$

2. **a.** James can ride 10 kilometers in 16 minutes. How long will it take him to ride 55 kilometers? Use the equivalent rates.

$$\dfrac{10 \text{ kilometers}}{16 \text{ minutes}} = \dfrac{5 \text{ kilometers}}{\boxed{} \text{ minutes}} = \dfrac{55 \text{ kilometers}}{\boxed{} \text{ minutes}}$$

b. How many kilometers can James ride in 40 minutes?

3. An automobile can go 80 kilometers on 8 liters of gasoline.

a. How many liters of gas would the automobile need for a trip of 95 kilometers? Use the equivalent rates below.

$$\dfrac{80 \text{ kilometers}}{8 \text{ liters}} = \dfrac{10 \text{ kilometers}}{\boxed{} \text{ liters}} = \dfrac{95 \text{ kilometers}}{\boxed{} \text{ liters}}$$

b. How far can the automobile travel on 15 liters of gas?

Example 2. You get 20 erasers for $5.00. How much would 22 erasers cost?

Cost (C)			$2.50	$5.00	
Erasers (E)	1	2	10	20	22

You can solve this problem in several ways. Let's use a table of rates this time.

First, find the cost for <u>10 erasers</u>, and then the cost for 2. After that, you can get the cost for 22 by adding.

Ten erasers will cost half of $5.00. Two erasers will cost one-fifth of that (divide by 5 to find it!). Lastly, add the cost of 20 erasers to the cost of 2 erasers to get the cost for 22 erasers.

Note 1: In the table, <u>each pair of numbers is a rate</u>. For example, $5.00 for 20 erasers (or $5.00/20 erasers) is a rate, and so is $2.50 for 10 erasers.

Note 2: Let's write an equation relating the Cost (C) and the number of Erasers (E). You will find that easily from the unit rate (the price for one): $C = 0.25E$. In other words, the cost is 0.25 times the number of erasers.

4. Finish solving the problem in the example above.

5. How many erasers would you get for $1.75?

6. On average, Scott makes a basket nine times out of twelve shots when he is practicing. How many baskets can he expect to make with 200 shots? A table of rates can help you solve this.

baskets						
shots						

7. **a.** Three pairs of socks cost $9. Fill in the table of rates. The variable C stands for cost, and p for pairs of socks.

C			9							
p	1	2	3	4	5	6	7	8	9	10

   b. Each number pair in the table *is* a rate, but we can also view them as <u>points</u> with two coordinates. Plot the number pairs in the coordinate grid.

   c. Write an equation relating the cost (C) and the number of pairs of socks (p).

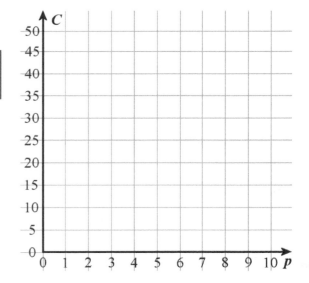

8. **a.** You get 30 pencils for $4.50. How much would 52 pencils cost?

Cost						
Pencils						

   b. Write an equation relating the cost (C) and the number of pencils (P).

9. When Kate makes 4 liters of tea (a pot full), she needs five jars for the tea. From this, we get the rate of 4 liters / 5 jars.

a. Fill in the table. The variable *t* stands for the amount of tea, and *j* for the number of jars.

t					4					
j	1	2	3	4	5	6	7	8	9	10

b. Plot the number pairs from the table in this coordinate grid.

c. How many jars will Kate need for 20 liters of tea?

d. If Kate has 16 jars full of tea, how many liters of tea is in them?

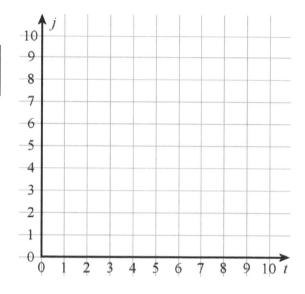

10. **a.** A train travels at a constant speed of 130 kilometers per hour. Fill in the table of rates.

d										
h	1	2	3	4	5	6	7	8	9	10

b. Write an equation relating the distance (*d*) and the number of hours (*h*).

c. Plot the points in the grid on the right. The variable *h* stands for hours, and *d* for distance.

11. Another train travels at the constant speed of 96 km per hour. Fill in the table of rates. Then, plot the points in the same coordinate grid as for the train in #10.

d					
h	1	2	3	4	5

d					
h	6	7	8	9	10

12. *How* can you see <u>from the graph</u> which train travels faster?

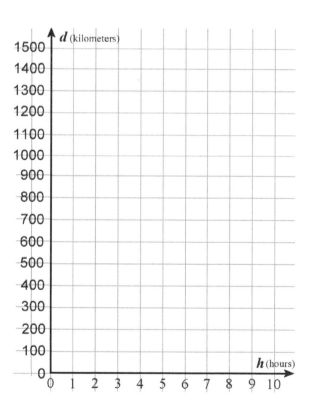

13. The plot shows the walking speed for two people (t is in minutes, d is in kilometers). Your task is to fill in the two ratio tables below. To make that easier, first find the dots that are at places where the lines cross, so that you can easily read the coordinates.

    (Hint: For some of the points, you will need to use decimals and whole numbers.)

Person 1 (red dot)

d (kilometers)										
t (minutes)										

Person 2 (blue dot)

d (kilometers)										
t (minutes)										

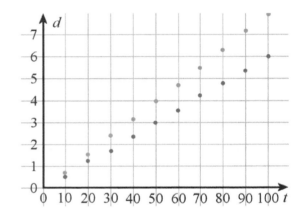

a. What is the speed of the first person in kilometers per hour?

b. What is the speed of the second person in kilometers per hour?

14. Train 1 travels at a constant speed of 165 miles in three hours. Train 2 travels 315 miles in seven hours. Which train is faster?

15. Find which is a better deal by comparing the unit rates: $45 for eight bottles of shampoo, or $34 for six bottles of shampoo?

16. In a poll of 1,000 people, 640 said they liked blue.

    a. Simplify this ratio to lowest terms:

    640 people *out of* 1,000 people = _____ people *out of* _____ people

    b. Assuming the same ratio holds true in another group of 100 people, how many of those people can we expect to like blue?

    c. Assuming the same ratio holds true in another group of 225 people, how many of those people can we expect to like blue?

Ratio Problems and Bar Models 1

Often, ratio problems become easy by drawing a **bar model**.

The ratio of blue shirts to green shirts to yellow shirts is 3 to 5 to 1. If there are 7,200 shirts in all, how many of them are of each color?

Look at the bar model. There are a total of 7,200 shirts.
We draw 3 "blocks" for the blue shirts, 5 "blocks" for the green shirts and 1 "block" for the yellow shirts to show the ratio of **3 : 5 : 1**. It is obvious one "block" means 7,200 ÷ 9 = 800 shirts. So there are a total of 2,400 blue shirts, 4,000 green shirts and 800 yellow shirts.

Juice concentrate is mixed with water in a ratio of 1:8. If you want to make 5 liters of juice, how much concentrate and how much water do you need?

Let's draw a bar model. (In reality, of course, the juice and water mix, but for the purpose of calculating, this model is helpful.)

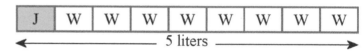

There are a total of 9 equal parts, so we simply
divide 5 liters by 9. First, change 5 liters to 5,000 milliliters, and then divide: 5,000 ml ÷ 9 ≈ 555.56 ml.

However, that is way too accurate. Measuring cups do not normally let us measure to the nearest milliliter, and not even to the nearest 10 milliliters, so let's round this to the nearest 50 ml to get 550 ml.

So we need 550 ml of juice concentrate and 5,000 ml − 550 ml = 4,450 ml of water.

1. A factory makes shirts in a ratio of 1:3:3:1 for the sizes S, M, L and XL, respectively.

   a. Draw a bar model. What is the ratio of small (S) shirts to the total number of shirts?

   b. In a batch of 1,000 shirts, how many of them are of each size?

2. The instructions on a box of juice concentrate say to mix 2 parts of concentrate to 5 parts of water.

   a. If you want to make 3 liters of juice, how much concentrate and how much water do you need?

   b. Let's say that you have 1/2 liter of concentrate left. According to the instructions, how much water would you need to add to that?

   How much diluted juice does this make?

3. Greg and Matthew worked on a project together. Matthew worked more than Greg did, so they agreed to divide the pay of $250 in a ratio of 3:5 (3 parts for Greg, and 5 parts for Matthew). Calculate how much each boy should get.

4. Ann and Shelley also worked on a project unequally. They decided to divide their pay in a ratio of 2:5 (2 parts for Ann, 5 parts for Shelly). If Ann received $80, calculate (a) how much Shelley got and (b) how much the total pay was.

5. A bag of marbles has white, translucent (clear) and colored marbles in a ratio of 1:3:5. If there are 75 colored marbles, find (a) how many marbles the bag has, (b) how many are white, and (c) how many are translucent (clear).

6. Samantha is making a large flower arrangement for a wedding decoration. She has white, red, yellow and pink roses in a ratio of 2:1:2:3. If she has 69 pink roses, what is the total number of roses in her arrangement?

7. A school has 24 teachers and 600 students.

   a. Write the ratio of teachers to students. Simplify it to lowest terms.

   b. To keep the same ratio of teachers to students, how many teachers should the school hire if the number of students increases to 800?

Fractions and ratios

Any ratio can be expressed using fractions instead. For example:

An automobile dealer's lot has Toyotas and Fords in a ratio of 2:3. We can express this ratio using fractions in *several* different ways:

Toyotas | T | T |

Fords | F | F | F |

- The number of Toyotas is 2/3 of the number of Fords.

- Toyotas are 2/5 of all the automobiles on the lot.

- Of all the automobiles on the lot, 3/5 are Fords.

8. A competitor's lot has Nissans and Fords. The number of Nissans is 4/5 of the number of Fords.

   a. What is the ratio of Nissans to Fords?

   b. What is the ratio of Fords to all automobiles?

   c. If there are 450 automobiles in all, how many are Fords?

Nissans

Fords

9. Joe had 3/5 as much money as Rita had.

   a. Draw a bar model to represent the situation.

   b. What was the ratio of Joe's money to Rita's money?

   c. Then Rita gave 1/5 of her money to Joe.
   Now what is the ratio of Joe's money to Rita's money?

10. Britney's weight is 5/6 of Joan's weight. If the two girls together weigh a total of 121 kg, how much does Britney weigh alone?

11. Fred had 2/9 as many marbles as Greg had.

   a. Draw a bar model to represent the situation.

   b. Greg gave 1/3 of his marbles to Fred. Draw another bar model to represent the new situation.

   c. If Greg has 120 marbles now, then how many marbles does Fred have now?

Ratio Problems and Bar Models 2

Example 1. Jack and Simon divided a reward in a ratio of 3:5. Simon got $80 <u>more</u> than Jack. How much was the total reward? How much did each boy get?

In this problem, we know the *difference* between how much Jack and Simon got. We draw Jack's and Simon's parts side-by-side. Jack gets 3 "blocks" and Simon gets 5 "blocks."

The *difference* is now easily seen from the model. Simon's part was 2 blocks more than Jack's, and those 2 blocks equal $80. Therefore, <u>1 block equals $40</u>.

So the total reward was 8 · $40 = 320, Jack got 3 · $40 = $120, and Simon got 5 · $40 = $200.

1. A crate of cell phones has red and silver models in a ratio of 2:7. There are 300 more silver phones than red ones.

   a. Draw a bar model to represent the situation.

   b. How many phones are in the crate?

   c. How many are red?

2. Eric and Erica collect phone cards, and their phone cards are in a ratio of 3:4. If Erica has 14 more phone cards than Eric, how many cards does Eric have?

3. The life spans of Mr. Short and Mr. Long were in a ratio of 3:7. Mr. Long lived 44 years longer than Mr. Short. How long did Mr. Long live?

4. Mark and Mary shared a sum of money in a ratio of 2:5. Then Mary gave 1/5 of her money to Mark. Now Mary has $30 more than Mark. What was the total sum of money?

Example 2. Amy and Betty shared a sum of $150 so that Betty got $24 more than Amy. How much did each girl get?

In this problem we know *the total*, and we know the *difference*, or how much more one person got than the other. This situation, too, is easily solved using a bar model.

Amy [?]
Betty [?][$24] } $150

The model shows the difference of $24 and the total of $150. A "?" marks the part that we don't know.

To solve this, imagine taking away the part of Betty's share that was more than Amy's share (the $24). Then the girls would have the same amount, and the total would be $126.

Amy [?]
Betty [?][$24] } $150 - $24 = $126

Now just find half of $126, or $63, which is the part marked with the "?" mark. That's what Amy got. Betty got $24 more than that, which is $87. Lastly, add $63 and $87 to make sure that you get $150.

5. Jonathan cut a 180-cm board into two pieces so that one piece was 50 cm longer than the other. How long are the pieces?

6. Mother divided 56 crayons so that Margie got 8 crayons more than her sister did. How many crayons did Margie get?

7. Jack bought 5 DVDs that cost the same and one DVD that cost $1 more than each of the others did. The total cost came to $72.40. Find the cost of the DVD that was more expensive than the others.

8. The lengths of three necklaces are in a ratio of 5:6:7. The longest necklace is 18 cm longer than the shortest necklace. How long are the necklaces?

These problems are a bit more challenging.

9. At first, the ratio of Alice's money to Cindy's money was 3:5.
   Then, they both spent $30. Now, the ratio of Alice's money to
   Cindy's money is 1:3. How much money did Alice have at first?

10. The ratio of the cookies in jar 1 to the cookies in jar 2 is 4:5.
    Mark moved 1/4 of the cookies from jar 1 to jar 2.
    Now, jar 2 has 24 cookies more than jar 1.
    How many cookies are there altogether?

11. Matthew had 2/3 as much money as John.
    Then John gave Matthew $5 for one of Matthew's sandwiches.
    Now the two boys have the same amount of money.
    How much money did John have in the beginning?

12. (This is the same problem as #11 above, but with one small difference.)
    Matthew had 2/3 as much money as John.
    Then John gave Matthew $5 for one of Matthew's sandwiches.
    Now the ratio of Matthew's money to John's money is 7:8.
    How much money did John have in the beginning?

13. Annie and Michelle were selling roses. Annie had 5/8 as many
    roses to sell as Michelle. After Michelle had sold half of her roses, and
    Annie had sold 21 of hers, Annie had 1/2 as many roses as Michelle.

    How many roses did Michelle have in the beginning?

Aspect Ratio

You might have heard about the <u>aspect ratio</u> of the screens of televisions, computer monitors and other monitors. The aspect ratio is simply **the ratio** of a **rectangle's width to its height or length.**

If the rectangle is "standing up," it is often easier to think and talk about width and height. If it is laid on the ground, then we usually talk about its width and length.

Example. A rectangle's width and height are in a ratio of 5:3. This means the aspect ratio is 5:3. If the rectangle's perimeter is 64 cm, what are its width and its height?

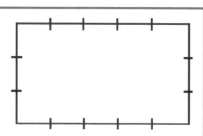

Let's draw the rectangle. Working from the 5:3 aspect ratio, let's divide the sides into "parts," or the same-sized segments, 5 for the width, and 3 for the height. We can see in the picture that perimeter is made up of 16 of these "parts." Since 64 ÷ 16 = 4, each part is 4 cm long.

Therefore, the rectangle's width is 5 · 4 cm = 20 cm, and its height is 3 · 4 cm = 12 cm.

1. The width and height of a rectangle are in a ratio of 9:2.

   a. Draw the rectangle, and divide its width and length into parts according to its aspect ratio.

   b. If the rectangle's perimeter is 220 cm, find its width and its height.

2. A rectangle's width is three times its length, and its perimeter is 120 mm. Find the rectangle's width and its length.

3. Find the aspect ratio of each rectangle:

   a. a rectangle whose height is 2/5 of its width

   b. a rectangle whose height is five times its width

   c. a square

4. The door of a refrigerator is 4/9 as wide as it is tall.

   a. What is the ratio of the door's width to its height?

   b. If the door is 54 cm wide, how tall is it?

5. Little Mary drew a picture on a rectangular piece of paper
   that was 15 centimeters wide and 25 centimeters long.

   a. Write the aspect ratio, and simplify it to the lowest terms.

   b. If this picture were enlarged to be 45 cm _wide_,
   how long would it be? Use equivalent ratios.

6. Mr. Miller is ordering custom-made windows for his new house. He is considering windows
   of these sizes: 70 cm × 90 cm, 80 cm × 100 cm, 90 cm × 110 cm, and 100 cm × 120 cm.

   a. Write the aspect ratios of all the windows
   and simplify them to lowest terms.

   b. Do any of the windows share exactly the same aspect ratio when simplified?
   If so, then which ones? (That would mean they would have exactly the same shape.)

7. A sandbox is two times as wide as it is long.

   a. What is its aspect ratio?

   b. The perimeter of the sandbox is 6 m.
   Find its length and width.

   c. Find its area.

> **Don't confuse area
> with perimeter.**
>
> The aspect ratio pertains
> to the _length_ and _width_,
> not to the area. However,
> once you know the length
> and the width, you can
> calculate the area.

8. Two television sets have the same perimeter, 150 cm. The aspect
   ratio of one is 16 : 9, and the aspect ratio of the other is 4 : 3.

   a. Find the length and width of each television.

   b. Which television has the larger area?

9. The area of a square is 49 cm^2. If two of these
   squares are put side by side, we get a rectangle.

   a. Find the aspect ratio of that rectangle.

   b. Find the perimeter of the rectangle.

Using Ratios to Convert Measuring Units

A calculator may be used in all of the exercises in this lesson.

Consider the conversion factor **1 inch = 2.54 cm** . If we think of it as an equation and divide both sides by "1 inch," then we will get 1 on the left side, and a RATIO on the right side:

$1 \text{ inch} = 2.54 \text{ cm}$	This is the conversion factor, but we will think of it as an equation now.
$\dfrac{1 \text{ inch}}{1 \text{ inch}} = \dfrac{2.54 \text{ cm}}{1 \text{ inch}}$	Divide both sides by "1 inch." Yes, we do include the unit *inch* in this.
$1 = \dfrac{2.54 \text{ cm}}{1 \text{ inch}}$	We get a plain 1 on the left side (something divided by itself equals 1).

What we get on the right side is the ratio <u>2.54 cm per 1 inch</u> (or 2.54 cm to 1 inch), and that ratio equals 1.

We can also do this the other way around:

$1 \text{ inch} = 2.54 \text{ cm}$	This is the conversion factor, but we will think of it as an equation now.
$\dfrac{1 \text{ inch}}{2.54 \text{ cm}} = \dfrac{2.54 \text{ cm}}{2.54 \text{ cm}}$	Divide both sides by "2.54 cm". Yes, we do include the unit *cm* in this.
$\dfrac{1 \text{ inch}}{2.54 \text{ cm}} = 1$	We get a plain 1 on the right side (something divided by itself equals 1).

What we get on the left side is the ratio <u>1 inch per 2.54 cm</u> (or 1 inch to 2.54 cm), and that ratio equals 1.

In fact, we can transform *any* conversion factor between measuring units into a ratio that is equal to 1.

1 qt = 0.946 L	0.946 L = 1 qt	1 mi = 1.6093 km	1 lb = 0.454 kg
↓	↓	↓	↓
$\dfrac{1 \text{ qt}}{0.946 \text{ L}} = 1$	$\dfrac{0.946 \text{ L}}{1 \text{ qt}} = 1$	$\dfrac{1 \text{ mi}}{1.6093 \text{ km}} = 1$	$\dfrac{1 \text{ lb}}{0.454 \text{ kg}} = 1$

1. Think of the conversion factors as equations, and transform each one into a new equation of the form
   "1 = a ratio" or "a ratio = 1."

1 ft = 0.3048 m	1 ounce = 28.35 g	1 mi = 1,760 yd	1 m = 1.0936 yd
↓	↓	↓	↓

We can use these ratios that equal one in **converting measuring units**.

How does that happen? Study the following example carefully. Mathematically speaking, we multiply the quantity we want to convert by 1. Multiplying it by 1 does not change its value. Then, we replace that 1 with one of the ratios of measuring units that equal 1. Next, we cross out the measuring units that cancel out. Lastly, we multiply/divide the numbers involved.

$$56 \text{ cm} = 56 \text{ cm} \cdot 1 = 56 \text{ cm} \cdot \frac{1 \text{ in}}{2.54 \text{ cm}} = 56 \,\cancel{\text{cm}} \cdot \frac{1 \text{ in.}}{2.54 \,\cancel{\text{cm}}} = \frac{56 \cdot 1 \text{ in}}{2.54} = 22.047 \text{ in} \approx 22 \text{ in.}$$

| Multiply the quantity by 1. | Replace that 1 with a ratio. | Cancel out the cm units. | Calculate. | Round. |

Notice that we **keep the the units of measure** in the calculation! The "cm" units cancel out, and we end up with only the unit "in" (which is what we wanted: to convert the given quantity into *inches*).

Another example, of converting 8.9 quarts into liters:

$$8.9 \text{ qt} = 8.9 \text{ qt} \cdot 1 = 8.9 \text{ qt} \cdot \frac{0.946 \text{ L}}{1 \text{ qt}} = 8.9 \,\cancel{\text{qt}} \cdot \frac{0.946 \text{ L}}{1 \,\cancel{\text{qt}}} = \frac{8.9 \cdot 0.946 \text{ L}}{1} = 8.4194 \text{ L} \approx 8.4 \text{ L}$$

| Multiply the quantity by 1. | Replace that 1 with a ratio. | Cancel out the qt units. | Calculate. | Round. |

2. Use the given ratios to convert the measuring units. Round your answers to one decimal digit.

a. Use $1 = \dfrac{2.54 \text{ cm}}{1 \text{ in}}$ to convert 79 inches to centimeters.

79 in =

b. Use $1 = \dfrac{1 \text{ mi}}{1.6093 \text{ km}}$ to convert 56 km to miles.

56 km =

c. Use $1 = \dfrac{1.6093 \text{ km}}{1 \text{ mi}}$ to convert 2.8 mi to kilometers.

2.8 mi =

d. Use $1 = \dfrac{0.946 \text{ L}}{1 \text{ qt}}$ to convert 4 qt to liters.

4 qt =

How do you know whether to use the ratio $\dfrac{1 \text{ in}}{2.54 \text{ cm}}$ or the ratio $\dfrac{2.54 \text{ cm}}{1 \text{ in}}$ when converting 7 inches into centimeters?

If the quantity you start with has inches, then you will need to cancel out the unit "inches" in the conversion. Therefore, choose the ratio that has inches <u>in the denominator</u>.

Here is an example of using the *wrong* ratio:

$$7 \text{ in} \; = \; 7 \text{ in} \cdot 1 \; = \; 7 \text{ in} \cdot \dfrac{1 \text{ in}}{2.54 \text{ cm}} \; = \; 7 \text{ in} \cdot \dfrac{1 \text{ in}}{2.54 \text{ cm}} \; = \; \dfrac{7 \text{ in} \cdot 1 \text{ in}}{2.54 \text{ cm}} \; = \; 2.7559 \text{ in}^2 / \text{cm}$$

| | Replace 1 with a ratio. | Nothing cancels. | Calculate. | The answer is not reasonable. Since inches are the longer units, 7 inches should convert to a bigger number of cm. The units didn't work out, either. |

Here are some conversion factors you will need in the following problems.

1 inch = 2.54 cm	1 yard = 0.9144 m	1 quart = 0.946 L	1 lb = 0.454 kg
1 foot = 0.3048 m	1 mile = 1.6093 km	1 ounce = 28.35 g	1 kg = 2.2 lb

3. Use ratios to convert the measuring units. Round your answers to one decimal digit.

a. 89 cm into inches

b. 15 kg into pounds

c. 78 miles into km

d. 89 feet into meters

e. 365 g into ounces

Chaining (optional). We can use TWO (or more) ratios in the conversion, and "chain" them together.

Example. Convert 0.9 liters into liquid ounces.

We have TWO conversion factors: 1 quart = 0.946 L and 1 quart = 32 oz. From these, we can write *four*

ratios: $\dfrac{1 \text{ qt}}{0.946 \text{ L}}$, $\dfrac{0.946 \text{ L}}{1 \text{ qt}}$, $\dfrac{32 \text{ oz}}{1 \text{ qt}}$, and $\dfrac{32 \text{ oz}}{1 \text{ qt}}$, all equaling 1. We can use TWO of those four, "chaining"

them together, to go from 0.9 liters to however many ounces:

$$0.9 \text{ L} = 0.9 \text{ L} \cdot \frac{1 \text{ qt}}{0.946 \text{ L}} \cdot \frac{32 \text{ oz}}{1 \text{ qt}} = 0.9 \text{ L} \cdot \frac{1 \text{ qt}}{0.946 \text{ L}} \cdot \frac{32 \text{ oz}}{1 \text{ qt}} = \frac{0.9 \cdot 32 \text{ oz}}{0.946} = \approx 30.4 \text{ oz.}$$

<table>
<tr><td>Write the two ratios
that equal 1.</td><td>Cancel out the
liters and quarts.</td><td>Calculate.</td><td>Round.</td></tr>
</table>

How do you choose which two of the possible four ratios to use? Since you start out with LITERS, you want a ratio where LITERS are in the denominator. And since you want to end up with OUNCES, you want a ratio where OUNCES are NOT in the denominator. The quarts and liters cancel out in the process, leaving the ounces.

4. Convert the measuring units as indicated.

a. Use the ratios (2.54 cm/1 in) and (12 in /1 ft) to convert 5 ft into centimeters. Round to the nearest cm.   5 ft =
b. Use the ratios (1 qt/32 oz) and (0.946 L/1 qt) to convert 24 oz into liters. Round to two decimals.
c. Convert 700 yards into meters. Round to one decimal.
d. Convert 8 kg into ounces (weight). Round to the nearest ounce.
e. Convert 371 ounces into grams. Round to the nearest 100 grams.
f. Convert 15 pints into liters. Round to two decimals.

Chapter 4 Mixed Review

1. Write the division equation, if the calculation
   to check it is $13 \cdot 381 + 5 = 4{,}958$.

   (Review of the Four Operations 1/Ch.1)

2. The fuel tank has 19.2 liters of gas left, and that
   is 3/10 of the volume of the tank.
   How much does the tank hold when full?
   (Lessons in Problem Solving/Ch.1)

3. Round to the place of the underlined digit. Be careful with the nines! (Rounding and Estimating/Ch.1)

   a. $51{,}9\underline{9}9{,}601 \approx$ _____

   b. $109{,}9\underline{9}9{,}339 \approx$ _____

4. **Multiply or divide in your head.** (Review: Multiply and Divide Decimals Mentally/Ch.3)

a. $3 \cdot 0.25 =$ _____	**b.** $8 \cdot 0.08 =$ _____	**c.** $1 \div 0.05 =$ _____	**d.** $0.99 \div 11 =$ _____
$4 \cdot 0.025 =$ _____	$100 \cdot 0.0008 =$ _____	$4 \div 0.05 =$ _____	$0.06 \div 0.001 =$ _____

5. **Multiply or divide the decimals by the powers of ten.** (Multiply and Divide by Powers of Ten/Ch.3)

a. $10^5 \cdot 3.07 =$	**b.** $10^4 \cdot 0.00078 =$
c. $12.7 \div 10^3 =$	**d.** $5{,}600 \div 10^5 =$

6. The area of a square is $4y^2$. What is the length of one side?
   (Writing and Simplifying Expressions 2/Ch.2)

7. Write 2,090,030 in expanded form using exponents.
   (Powers and Exponents/Ch.1)

8. **Fill in the table.** (More on Writing and Simplifying Expressions/Ch.2)

Expression	the terms in it	coefficient(s)	Constants
$2a + 3b$			
$10s$			
$11x + 5$			
$8x^2 + 9x + 10$			
$\dfrac{1}{6}p$			

9. Xavier and Yvonne got 10 small cookies from their mother to share. They did not have to share them equally. Let us consider the cookies Xavier got (X) and the cookies Yvonne got (Y).

   a. Fill in the table with possible values for X and Y, and plot the points in the grid.

X									
Y									

   b. Write an equation that relates X and Y.

   c. Which of the two variables is the independent variable?

10. Write an expression for each situation. (Expressions, Part 1/Ch.2)

   a. The value, in cents, of t ten-cent coins (t is a whole number).

   b. You have 67 drawings and you throw away y of them. How many do you have now?

   c. The original price of a puzzle is p. Now it is discounted and costs only 8/10 as much. What is the current price?

11. Divide, giving your answer as a decimal. If necessary, round the answers to three decimal digits.
(Review: Long Division with Decimals/Ch.3)

a. $675.5 \div 0.3$	**b.** $\dfrac{2}{7}$

Chapter 4 Review

1. Write the equivalent ratios.

a. $\dfrac{4}{3} = \dfrac{20}{}$	**b.** $6 : 7 = 18 : \underline{\hspace{1cm}}$	**c.** $\underline{\hspace{1.5cm}}$ to $30 = 2$ to 15	**d.** $\dfrac{7}{3} = \dfrac{}{12}$

2. Simplify the ratios.

a. $\dfrac{15}{35} = \dfrac{}{}$	**b.** $\dfrac{6}{16} = \dfrac{}{}$	**c.** $33 : 30 = \underline{\hspace{0.6cm}} : \underline{\hspace{0.6cm}}$	**d.** $9 : 12 = \underline{\hspace{0.6cm}} : \underline{\hspace{0.6cm}}$

3. **a.** Draw a picture where there are 2 hearts for each 3 triangles and a total of 15 triangles.

   b. Fill in the unit rates:

   $\underline{\hspace{2cm}}$ hearts for **1** triangle

   $\underline{\hspace{2cm}}$ triangles for **1** heart

4. A car traveled 480 kilometers in 6 hours at a constant speed. Fill in the table of equivalent rates:

Km					
Hours	1	2	3	4	5

Km					
Hours	6	7	8	9	10

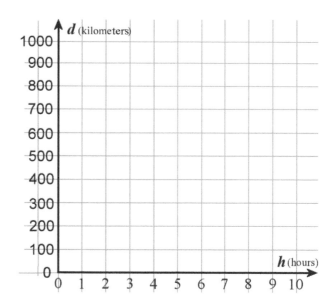

   a. Plot the points in the coordinate grid.

   b. What is the unit rate?

   c. How far would the car go at that speed in 7 ½ hours?

   d. How long would it take for it to travel 440 kilometers?

5. A mixture of salt and water contains 20 grams of salt and 1,200 grams of water.

    a. Write the ratio of salt to water, and simplify it to lowest terms.

    b. Use the same ratio of salt to water. If there are 100 grams
       of salt, how many grams of water would be needed?

6. Mother and Father's ages are in a ratio of 11:12. Father is 3 years older than Mother.
   How old are Mother and Father?

7. A bean plant is 3/5 as tall as a tomato plant. The tomato plant is 20 cm taller than the bean plant.

    a. What is the ratio of the bean plant's height to the tomato plant's height?

    b. How tall is the bean plant? The tomato plant?

8. The aspect ratio of a television screen is 16:9 (width to height),
   and it is 63 cm high. What is its width?

9. **a.** If 12 kg of chicken feed costs $20, how much would 5 kg cost?

    b. What is the unit rate? (price per 1 kg)

10. Use ratios to convert the measuring units. 1 kg = 2.2 lb, and 1 ft = 30.48 cm. Round to one decimal digit.

a. 134 lb into kilograms
b. 156 cm into feet

Chapter 5: Percent
Introduction

This chapter is all about the basics of the concept of percent—a very important topic in regards to real life. We focus on how to calculate percentages (e.g. what percentage is $20 of $50) and how to find a certain percentage of a given number or quantity (e.g. what is 20% of 80 km). In seventh grade, students learn about percent of change and how to make comparisons with percent.

The lessons emphasize the connection between percentages and fractions and decimals in various ways. After all, percentages *are* fractions: the word percent simply means "a hundredth part," and the concept of percent builds on the student's previous understanding of fractions and decimals.

Specifically, the student should be very familiar with the idea of finding a fractional part of a whole (such as finding 3/4 of $240). Students using Math Mammoth have been practicing that concept since fourth grade, and one reason why I have emphasized finding a fractional part of a whole in the earlier grades is specifically to lay a groundwork for the concept of percent. Assuming the student has mastered that, and can easily convert fractions to decimals, then studying the concept of percent should not be difficult.

In this context of thinking of percentages as fractions, students learn how to find a percentage of a given number or quantity using **mental math techniques**. For example, students find 10% of $400 by thinking of it as 1/10 of $400, and thus dividing $400 by 10. They also learn to find a percentage of a quantity using *decimal* multiplication, both manually and with a calculator. For example, students find 17% of 45 km by multiplying 0.17×45 km.

In fact, in cases where mental math is not a good option, I prefer teaching students to calculate percentages of quantities using decimals, instead of using percent proportion or fractions. That is because using decimals is simpler and quicker. Also, this method is often superior later on in algebra courses, when students need to write equations from verbal descriptions, and symbolically represent situations that involve percentages.

The last lesson of the chapter teaches students how to find the total when the percentage and the partial amount are known. For example: "Three-hundred twenty students, which is 40% of all students, take PE. How many students are there in total?" Students solve these with the help of the visual bar models, which they are already familiar with.

As the lessons constantly refer back to fractions and decimals, students can relate calculations with percentages to their earlier knowledge, and thus see **the logical structure of mathematics**. It will also prevent students from memorizing calculations with percentages without understanding what is going on.

As a reminder, it is not recommended that you assign all the exercises by default. Use your judgment, and strive to vary the number of assigned exercises according to the student's needs. Some students might only need half or even less of the available exercises, in order to understand the concepts.

You will find free videos covering many topics of this chapter at https://www.mathmammoth.com/videos/.

The Lessons in Chapter 5

	page	span
Percent	173	*4 pages*
What Percentage...?	177	*2 pages*
Percentage of a Number (Mental Math)	179	*3 pages*
Percentage of a Number: Using Decimals	182	*3 pages*
Discounts	185	*2 pages*

	page	span
Practice with Percent	187	*3 pages*
Finding the Total When the Percent Is Known	190	*2 pages*
Chapter 5 Mixed Review	192	*2 pages*
Review: Percent	194	*2 pages*

Helpful Resources on the Internet

We have compiled a list of Internet resources that match the topics in this chapter. This list of links includes web pages that offer:

- **online practice** for concepts;
- online **games**, or occasionally, printable games;
- **animations** and interactive **illustrations** of math concepts;
- **articles** that teach a math concept.

We heartily recommend you take a look at the list. Many of our customers love using these resources to supplement the bookwork. You can use the resources as you see fit for extra practice, to illustrate a concept better and even just for some fun. Enjoy!

https://l.mathmammoth.com/gr6ch5

SCAN ME

Percent

Percent (or **per cent**) means *per hundred* or "divided by a hundred."
That is because the word "cent" means one hundred.

The symbol for percent is **%**.

When you divide by 100, you get one hundredth (1/100).
Therefore, 8% means 8 per 100, which is 8/100.
Similarly, 67% means 67 divided by 100, or 67/100.

$$\frac{5}{100} \begin{array}{l} \text{five} \\ \text{per} \\ \text{cent} \end{array} = 5\%$$

Since percentages are just hundredths, we can very easily write them as fractions and as decimals.

$$63\% = \frac{63}{100} = 0.63 \qquad\qquad 9\% = \frac{9}{100} = 0.09$$

1. Write the shaded part and the unshaded part as fractions, as decimals and as percentages.

a.	shaded		**b.**	shaded
	$\frac{\quad}{\quad}$ = _____ = _____ %			$\frac{\quad}{\quad}$ = _____ = _____ %
	unshaded			unshaded
	$\frac{\quad}{\quad}$ = _____ = _____ %			$\frac{\quad}{\quad}$ = _____ = _____ %

2. Write as percentages, fractions and decimals.

a. $28\% = \frac{28}{100} = 0.28$	**b.** $17\% = \frac{\quad}{\quad} = $ _____	**c.** _____ $\% = \frac{\quad}{\quad} = 0.89$
d. $60\% = \frac{\quad}{\quad} = $ _____	**e.** _____ $\% = \frac{5}{100} = $ _____	**f.** _____ $\% = \frac{\quad}{\quad} = 0.08$

3. Typically, seven out of every 100 babies born in the River Creek Hospital have a birth defect, most of them minor defects.

   a. What typical percentage of the babies have birth defects?

   b. What typical percentage of the babies do *not* have birth defects?

   c. About how many babies with birth defects would you expect to find in a group of 500 babies?

   d. About how many babies with birth defects would you expect to find in a group of 1,300 babies?

<table>
<tr><td colspan="2" align="center">Other fractions as percentages</td></tr>
</table>

What part of the pencils are short? 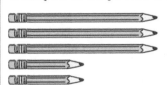 Two out of five, or 2/5 of them are short.	Let's rewrite 2/5 with a denominator of 100 using the method for equivalent fractions: 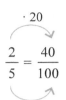 Now we can write 40/100 as 40%. So, 40% of the pencils are short.

4. Write what part of the pencils are short, both as a fraction and as a percentage. Use equivalent fractions.

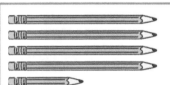

a. $\dfrac{}{} = \dfrac{}{100} = $ _____% **b.** $\dfrac{}{} = \dfrac{}{100} = $ _____% **c.** $\dfrac{}{} = \dfrac{}{100} = $ _____%

5. Convert the fractions into equivalent fractions with a denominator of 100, and then write them as percentages.

a. $\dfrac{4}{10} = \dfrac{}{100} = $ _____%	**b.** $\dfrac{11}{20} = \dfrac{}{100} = $ _____%	**c.** $\dfrac{8}{10} = \dfrac{}{100} = $ _____%
d. $\dfrac{3}{20} = \dfrac{}{100} = $ _____%	**e.** $\dfrac{6}{25} = \dfrac{}{100} = $ _____%	**f.** $\dfrac{4}{5} = \dfrac{}{100} = $ _____%

6. Write what part of the rectangle is shaded and what part is not shaded, both as fractions and percentages.

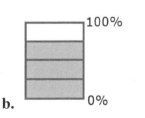

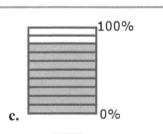

a.
Shaded: $\dfrac{}{} = $ _____%

Not shaded: $\dfrac{}{} = $ _____%

b.
Shaded: $\dfrac{}{} = $ _____%

Not shaded: $\dfrac{}{} = $ _____%

c.
Shaded: $\dfrac{}{} = $ _____%

Not shaded: $\dfrac{}{} = $ _____%

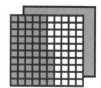

Percentages that are more than 100%

The image shows 1 whole and 55/100. As a mixed number, we write 1 55/100. As a decimal, we write 1.55.

Since 55/100 is 55%, and one whole is 100%, the image shows 155%.

We can use percentages that are more than 100%. Just remember that 100% is 1, and 1% is 0.01.

$$200\% = \frac{200}{100} = 2 \qquad\qquad 308\% = \frac{308}{100} = 3.08$$

7. Write as fractions, decimals and percentages.

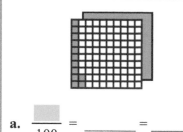

a. $\dfrac{}{100}$ = _____ = _____%

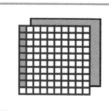

b. $\dfrac{}{100}$ = _____ = _____%

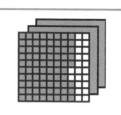

c. $\dfrac{}{100}$ = _____ = _____%

8. Write as percentages, fractions and decimals.

a. $105\% = \dfrac{}{}$ = _____	**b.** $457\% = \dfrac{}{}$ = _____	**c.** ____% $= \dfrac{}{} = 2.09$
d. ____% $= \dfrac{506}{100}$ = _____	**e.** ____% $= \dfrac{482}{100}$ = _____	**f.** ____% $= \dfrac{}{} = 3.11$

9. Write the fractions as percentages.

  a. About 4/5 (_____ %) of the population of the United States is 14 years old or older.

  b. About 2/25 (_____ %) of the world's population lives in North America.

  c. The continent of Africa covers about 1/5 (_____ %) of the Earth's total land mass.

10. There are two trees growing in Sandy's front yard. The taller one is 5/4 as tall as the shorter one.

  a. Write the second sentence using a percentage instead of a fraction.

  b. If the shorter tree is 160 cm tall, how tall is the taller tree?

Change any fraction to a percentage

To write 1/7 as a percentage, you can either:

- Divide 1 by 7 using long division or a calculator. You will get a decimal number. Express that as a percentage. OR,

- Find 1/7 of 100%; in other words divide 100 by 7. Then your answer is already a percentage.

```
    0 1 4 . 2 8
7 ) 1 0 0 . 0 0
  - 7
    3 0
  - 2 8
      2 0
    - 1 4
        6 0
      - 5 6
          4
```

Dividing 100 by 7, we get 14.28...
Rounded to the nearest whole percent, that is 14%.

How many percent would 2/7 be?
What about 5/7?

11. Write the fractions as percentages. Use long division. Round your answers to the nearest percent.

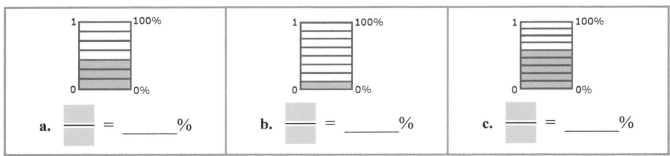

a. ———— = _____ %   **b.** ———— = _____ %   **c.** ———— = _____ %

12. Write the fractions as percentages. Round the answers to the nearest percent.

a. According to a 2020 estimate, about 1/20 (_____ %) of the population of Guatemala is 65 years old or older.

b. In that same year, about 13/100 (_____ %) of the population of Australia was 65 years old or older.

c. The Indian Ocean covers approximately 7/50 (_____ %) of the Earth's surface.

d. About 3/5 (_____ %) of the world's population lives in Asia.

13. Write as a percentage. Round your answers to the nearest percent.

a. 8/7   **b.** 1 3/8

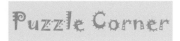

How many percent of each figure is colored?

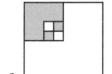 a.

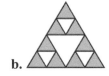 b.

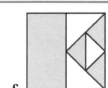 c.

What Percentage...?

What percentage of the height of a 4-m tree is a 1-m sapling?	A choir has 22 women and 18 men. **Find what percentage** of the choir's members are men.	One pair of jeans costs $25 and another costs $28. **How many percent** is the price of the cheaper jeans of the price of the more expensive jeans?

Look carefully at the questions above. Notice that the problems don't tell you the percentage; in other words, there is no number in the problem written as *x*%. Instead, they ask *you* to find it!

Questions with "What percentage...?" or "How many percent...?"

Asking "What percentage?" or "How many percent?" is the same as asking "How many hundredth parts?"

We can solve these questions in a two-part process:

1. First find out the part that is being asked for <u>as a fraction</u>. The denominator will probably not be 100.

2. Convert that fraction to a decimal. Then you can easily convert the decimal to a percentage!

Example 1. A choir has 22 women and 18 men. Find what percentage of the choir's members are men.

1. Find *what part* (fraction) of the choir's members are men. That is 18/40, or 9/20.

2. Write 9/20 as a percentage. You can use equivalent fractions: 9/20 = 45/100 = 45%.

Example 2. One pair of jeans costs $25 and another costs $28.
How many percent is the price of the cheaper jeans of the price of the more expensive jeans?

1. Write *what part* (fraction) the cheaper price is of the more expensive price. The answer is 25/28.

2. Write 25/28 as a percentage. A calculator gives 25/28 = 0.8928...
   Rounded to the nearest whole percent, that is 89%.

---

1. **a.** What percentage of the height of a 4-m tree is the height of a little 1-m sapling?

   b. How many percent is $12 of $16?

2. Find how many percent the shorter object's height is of the taller object's height.

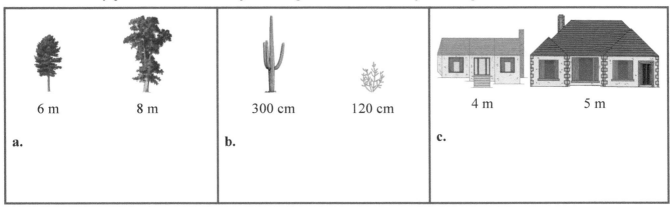

6 m 8 m	300 cm 120 cm	4 m 5 m
a.	**b.**	**c.**

3. A 2-year old child measures 80 centimeters tall and weighs 11 kilograms.
   A 10-year old child measures 130 cm (1.30 m) tall and weighs 44 kilograms.

   a. How many percent is the smaller child's
   age of the older child's age?

   b. How many percent is the smaller child's
   height of the older child's height?

   c. What percentage is the smaller child's
   weight of the older child's weight?

4. Write the *approximate* percentages into the sectors in the circle graphs. Think of fractions!

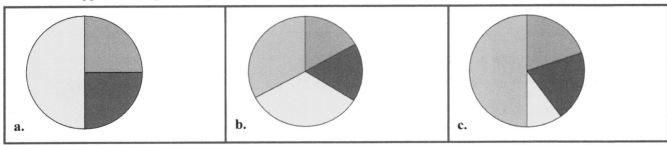

a.
b.
c.

5. The circle graph at the right gives the angle measure of each sector
   of the circle. Find what percentage each sector is of the whole circle.
   Lastly, write that percentage *in* the sector in the image. Remember, the
   whole circle is 360°.
   Hint: Think what percentage 117° is of 360°.

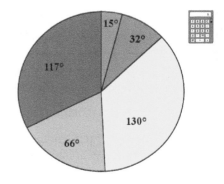

6. Nine hundred sixty people gathered at a medical conference. Of them, 450 were
   doctors, 220 were nurses and the rest were researchers. Find what percentage of
   the people were doctors, what percentage were nurses and what percentage were
   researchers.

Puzzle Corner

Draw or sketch a circle
graph to represent the
situation in exercise #6.

Percentage of a Number (Mental Math)

100% of something means *all* of it.   1% of something means 1/100 of it.

Since one percent means "a hundredth part," calculating a percentage of a quantity is the same thing as finding a fractional part of it. So **percentages are really fractions**!

How much is 1% of 200 kg? This means how much is 1/100 of 200 kg? It is simply 2 kg.

To find 1% of something (1/100 of something), divide by 100.

Do you remember how to divide by 100 in your head? Just move the decimal point two places to the left. For example, 1% of 540 is 5.4, and 1% of 8.30 is 0.083.

To find 2% of some quantity, first find 1% of it, and double that.

For example, let's find 2% of $6. Since 1% of $6 is $0.06, then 2% of $6 is $0.12.

To find 10% of some quantity, divide by 10.

Why does that work? It is because 10% is 10/100, which equals 1/10. So 10% is 1/10 of the quantity!

For example, 10% of $780 is $78. And 10% of $6.50 is $0.65.
(To divide by 10 in your head, just move the decimal point one place to the left.)

Can you think of a way to find 20% of a number?

_____

1. Find 10% of these numbers.

    a. 700 _____   **b.** 321 _____   **c.** 60 _____   **d.** 7 _____

2. Find 1% of these numbers.

    a. 700 _____   **b.** 321 _____   **c.** 60 _____   **d.** 7 _____

3. One percent of Mother's paycheck is $22. How much is her total paycheck?

4. Fill in the table. Use mental math.

percentage ↓ number →	1,200	80	29	9	5.7
1% of the number					
2% of the number					
10% of the number					
20% of the number					

5. Fill in this guide for using mental math with percentages:

Mental Math and Percentage of a Number	
50% is $\frac{1}{2}$**. To find 50% of a number, divide by** _____.	50% of 244 is _____.
10% is $\frac{1}{\boxed{}}$**. To find 10% of a number, divide by** _____.	10% of 47 is _____.
1% is $\frac{1}{\boxed{}}$**. To find 1% of a number, divide by** _____.	1% of 530 is _____.
To find 20%, 30%, 40%, 60%, 70%, 80%, or 90% of a number, • **First find** _____ **% of the number, and** • **then multiply by 2, 3, 4, 6, 7, 8, or 9.**	10% of 120 is _____. 30% of 120 is _____. 60% of 120 is _____.

6. Find the percentages. Use mental math.

a. 10% of 60 kg _____ 20% of 60 kg _____	**b.** 10% of $14 _____ 30% of $14 _____	**c.** 10% of 5 m _____ 40% of 5 m _____
d. 1% of $60 _____ 4% of $60 _____	**e.** 10% of 110 cm _____ 70% of 110 cm _____	**f.** 1% of $1,330 _____ 3% of $1,330 _____

7. David pays a 20% income tax on his $2,100 salary.

   a. How many dollars is the tax?

   b. How much money does he have left after paying the tax?

   c. What percentage of his salary does he have left?

8. Nancy pays 30% of her $3,100 salary in taxes. How much money does she have left after paying the tax?

9. Identify the errors that these children made. Then find the correct answers.

a. Find 90% of $55. Peter's solution: 10% of $55 is $5.50 So, I subtract 100% − $5.50 = $94.50	**b.** Find 6% of $1,400. Patricia's solution: 1% of $1,400 is $1.40. So, 6% is six times that, or $8.40.

Some more mental math "tricks"	
90% of a quantity First find 10% of the quantity and then subtract that from 100% of it.	**25% of a quantity** 25% is the same as 1/4. So, to find 25% of a quantity, divide it by 4.
12% of a quantity First find 10% of it. Then find 1% of it, and use that 1% to find 2% of it. Then add the 10% and the 2%.	**75% of a quantity** 75% is 3/4. First find 1/4 of the quantity and multiply that by 3.

10. Find percentages of the quantities.

a. 50% of 26 cm _____	**b.** 25% of 40 mm _____	**c.** 80% of 45 m _____
d. 75% of $4.40 _____	**e.** 90% of 1.2 m _____	**f.** 25% of 120 kg _____

11. Fill in the mental math method for finding 12% of $65.

   10% of $65 is $_____.   1% of $65 is $_____.   2% of $65 is $_____.

   Now, add to get 12% of $65: $_____ + $_____ = $_____

12. Fill in the mental math shortcut for finding 24% of 44 kg.

   25% of 44 kg is _____ kg.   1% of 44 kg is _____ kg.

   Subtract _____ kg − _____ kg = _____ kg

13. From her cell phone bill, Hannah sees that of the 340 text messages she sent last month, 15% were sent during the night at a cheaper rate. How many messages did Hannah send at night? During the day?

14. A herd of 40 horses had some bay, some chestnut and some white horses. Thirty percent of them are bay, and 45% are chestnut. How many horses are white?

15. A college has 1,500 students, and 12% of them ride the bus. Another 25% walk to the college. How many students do not do either?

Percentage of a Number: Using Decimals

You have learned that finding 1% of a number means finding 1/100 of it. Similarly, finding 60% of a number means finding 60/100 (or 6/10) of it.

In these types of expressions, the word "of" translates into **multiplication**:

1% of 90		60% of $700
↓	OR	↓
1% · 90		60% · $700

Next, let's write those percentages as *decimals*. We get:

1% of 90		60% of $700
↓	OR	↓
0.01 · 90		0.6 · $700

This gives us another way to calculate a certain percentage of a number (or a percentage of some quantity):

To calculate a percentage of a number, you need to make TWO simple changes:

1. **Change the percentage into a decimal.**

2. **Change the word "of" into multiplication.**

Example 1. Find 70% of 80.

Making the two changes, we write this as 0.7 · 80.

(Remember, in decimal multiplication, you multiply just as if there were no decimal points, and the answer will have as many decimal digits as the total number of decimal digits in all of the factors.)

So, when you multiply 0.7 · 80, think of multiplying 7 · 80 = 560. Since 0.7 has one decimal digit, and 80 has none, the answer has one decimal digit. Thus, 0.7 · 80 = 56.0 or just 56.

You can also use common sense and estimation: 0.7 · 80 must be less than 80, yet more than 1/2 of 80, which is 40. Since 7 · 8 = 56, you know that the answer must be 56—not 5.6 or 560.

Example 2. Find 3% of $4,000.

First, write this as 0.03 · $4,000. Next, multiply without decimal points: 3 · $4,000 = $12,000. Lastly, put the decimal point so that the answer will have two decimal digits: $120.00.

Example 3. Find 23% of 5,500 km.

Write this as 0.23 · 5,500 km and use a calculator. The answer is 1,265 km. This makes sense, because 10% of 5,500 km is 550 km, and 20% of it is 1,100 km. Therefore, 1,265 km as 23% of 5,500 km is reasonable.

1. "Translate" the expressions into multiplications by a decimal. Solve, using mental math.

a. 20% of 70	**b.** 90% of 50	**c.** 80% of 400
_____ · _____ = _____	_____ · _____ = _____	_____ · _____ = _____
d. 60% of $8	**e.** 9% of 3,000	**f.** 7% of 40 L
_____ · _____ = _____	_____ · _____ = _____	_____ · _____ = _____
g. 150% of 44 kg	**h.** 200% of 56 students	**i.** 2% of 1,500 km
_____ · _____ = _____	_____ · _____ = _____	_____ · _____ = _____

2. "Translate" the other way: Write the multiplications as expressions of a "percentage of the number".

a. 0.6 · 50 _____% of _____ = _____	**b.** 0.03 · $400 _____% of _____ = _____	**c.** 0.8 · 400 km _____% of _____ = _____
d. 0.08 · 6 _____% of _____ = _____	**e.** 0.11 · $300 _____% of _____ = _____	**f.** 0.2 · 70 kg _____% of _____ = _____

3. Use a calculator to find percentages of these quantities.

  a. 17% of $4,500   **b.** 67% of 27 m   **c.** 48% of 7.8 kg

4. Use mental math to find percentages of these quantities.

  a. 25% of 240 m   **b.** 80% of 30,000 km   **c.** 75% of 3.2 kg

5. **a.** A lake has a 30-km long shoreline. Six percent of it is sandy beach.
    What *percentage* of the shoreline is *not* sandy beach?

  b. Find the length (in km) of the shoreline that *is* sandy beach.

6. Twenty percent of a university's 4,000 students have a scholarship.

  a. What *percentage* of the students do *not* have a scholarship?

  b. How many students have a scholarship?

  c. How many students do *not* have a scholarship?

7. A farmer had 1,200 hectares of land. He planted 30% of it
  with wheat, 45% with corn and the rest with oats.
  Find how many hectares he planted with each kind of grain.

8. Identify the errors that these children made. Then find the correct answers.

a. Find 80% of 50.	**b.** Find 75% of 84,000.
Gladys's solution: $80 \cdot 50 = 4{,}000$	Glenn's solution: This is the same as $84{,}000 \div 4 = 21{,}000$.

9. Circle the expressions with the same value as 20% of $620.

$0.02 \cdot \$620$ $\$620 \div 5$ $\$620 \div 10 \cdot 2$ $2 \cdot \$62$

$\dfrac{1}{5} \cdot \$620$ $0.2 \cdot \$620$ $20 \cdot \$620$ $\$620 \div 4$

10. About 69% of Italy's population of 60 million live in cities.
About 37% of Tanzania's population of 60 million live in cities.

How many more Italians than Tanzanians live in cities?

11. The table below shows Andy's usage of time in one day.

    a. Calculate the time he spent doing each activity. Round the minutes to the nearest minute.

    b. Label the sections in the circle graph with the name of each activity.

Andy's Usage of Time

Activity	Percentage	Minutes	Hours/minutes
Sleep	38%		
School	21%		
Soccer	10%	144	2 h 24 min
Play	11%		
Eating	9%		
Chores	9%		
Hygiene	2%		
TOTAL	100%	1440	24 hours

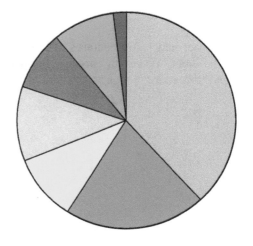

Discounts

Other than figuring sales tax, the area of life in which you will probably most often need to use percentages is in calculating discounts.

A laptop that costs $600 is 20% off. What is the sale price?

Method 1. We calculate 20% of $600. That is the discounted amount in *dollars*.
Then we subtract that from the original price, $600.

20% of $600 is $120. And $600 − $120 = $480. So the sale price is $480.

Method 2. Since 20% of the price has been removed, 80% of the price is *left*.
By calculating 80% of the original price, you will get the new discounted price: 0.8 · $600 = $480

Two methods for calculating the discounted price:

1. Calculate the discount amount as a percentage of the original price. Then subtract.

2. Find what percentage of the price is left. Then calculate that percentage of the normal price.

1. All of these items are on sale. Calculate the discount in dollars and the resulting sale price.

a. Price: $90 20% off	**b.** Price: $5 40% off	**c.** Price: $15 30% off
Discount amount: $___18___	Discount amount: $_____	Discount amount: $_____
Sale price: $_____	Sale price: $_____	Sale price: $_____

2. A swimsuit that cost $25, was on sale for 20% off.
   Monica tried to calculate the discounted price this way: $25 − $20 = $5.
   What did she do wrong? Find the correct discounted price.

3. All these items are on sale. Find the discounted price.

a. Price: $1.20 25% off	**b.** Price: $18 25% off	**c.** Price: $150 30% off
Discount amount: $_____	Discount amount: $_____	Discount amount: $_____
Discounted price: $_____	Discounted price: $_____	Discounted price: $_____
d. Price: $20 40% off	**e.** Price: $4.00 10% off	**f.** Price: $1.30 50% off
Discount amount: $_____	Discount amount: $_____	Discount amount: $_____
Discounted price: $_____	Discounted price: $_____	Discounted price: $_____

You can often use **estimation** when calculating the discounted price.

Example 1. A bicycle that costs $198.95 is discounted by 25%. What is the discounted price?

To estimate, round the original price of the bicycle to $200. Then, 25% of $200 is $50 (it is ¼ of it). So the discounted price is about $150.

Example 2. A laptop that costs $425.90 is discounted by 28%. What is the discounted price?

Round the discount percentage to 30%, and the price of the laptop to $430. 10% of $430 is $43. 30% of $430 is three times that much, or $129. Subtract using rounded numbers: $430 − $130 = $300.

4. *Estimate* the discounted price.

   a. 30% off of a book that costs $39.90

   b. 17% off of a sandwich that costs $12.50

   c. 75% off of a swimming cap that costs $75.50

5. Which is a better deal? Estimate using rounded numbers and mental math.

   a. 75% off of a brand-name mp3 player that costs $199
   OR an equivalent off-brand mp3 player for $44.99.

   b. 40% off of a new textbook that costs $89
   OR a used copy, like new, of the same textbook for $39.90.

6. A company sells an app for $9.99. They estimate they would sell
   50 copies of it in a week, with that price. If they discount
   the price by 25%, they think they could sell 100 copies.
   Estimate which way they would earn the most money.

Example 3. A $50 pair of shoes is discounted and now costs only $35. What is the discount percentage?

Think about what *fraction* of the price "disappeared." Then, write that fraction as a percentage.

We see that $15 of the price "went away." The <u>fraction</u> of the price that was taken off is thus 15/50. Now we simply rewrite 15/50 as 30/100, which is, as a percentage, 30%. So it was discounted by 30%.

7. Find the discount percentage.

   a. Some jeans: original price, $50; discounted price, $45.

   b. A phone: original price, $40; discounted price, $30.

   c. A haircut: original price, $25; discounted price, $20.

8. Which of these methods work for calculating a discounted price of 25% off of $46?

$0.25 \cdot \$46$	$0.75 \cdot \$46$	$\$46 - \dfrac{\$46}{25}$	$\$46 - \dfrac{\$46}{4}$	$\dfrac{\$46}{4}$	$\dfrac{\$46}{4} \cdot 3$

Practice with Percent

1. What is 70% of $380?	2. What percentage is $70 of $380?
Notice *carefully* the difference between the two questions above! Question #1 asks for a certain part (70/100) of $380, and the answer will be in dollars. Question #2 asks for the percentage.	

1. What is 70% of $380?	2. What percentage is $70 of $380?
First we find 10% of $380. That is just 1/10 of it, or $38. Then we multiply that by 7 to get 70% of $380: 7 · $38 = $266. So 70% of $380 is $266. Alternatively, you could multiply 0.7 · $380 = $266.	First we write what part $70 is of $380. It is simply 70/380 or 7/38. Writing this fraction as a decimal, 7/38 = 0.184210526 ≈ 0.18, which is 18%.

If the percentage is known, and the total is known: (What is x% of y?)	If the percentage is unknown: ("What percentage?" / "How many percent?")
1. Write the percentage as a decimal. 2. Multiply that decimal and the number. Or use mental math tricks for finding 1%, 10%, 20%, 30%, 25%, 50%, 75%, *etc.* of a number.	1. Write the part asked for <u>as a fraction</u>. 2. Convert the fraction to a decimal → percentage.

1. **a.** Find 10% of $50.

   b. What percentage of $50 is $10?

2. **a.** Jenny ate 60% of a package of 25 cookies.
   How many cookies did Jenny eat?

   b. Jared ate 6 of the 25 cookies in the package.
   What percentage of the cookies did Jared eat?

3. Use mental math to fill in the missing numbers:

a. Jack made 17 baskets out of 20 shots. Jack made baskets on ⬜, or _____%, of his shots.	**b.** Jack made baskets on 56% of 50 shots. Jack made _____ baskets in all.
c. Of 25 women surveyed, 60% like chocolate. Of those 25, _____ women like chocolate.	**d.** 42 out of 200 citizens voted for Mr. X. _____% of the citizens voted for Mr. X.
e. Of 1,000 boxes, 620 contained books. _____% of the boxes contained books.	**f.** Out of 50 participants, 14% came late. So, _____ participants came late.

A **diagram** (bar model) can keep you from getting confused with fractions, percentages and actual quantities.

Example 1. 18 out of 25 swimmers in the club are practicing freestyle.
How many percent of the swimmers are practicing freestyle?

Each swimmer is one "block" in the diagram. The whole diagram represents 25 swimmers, but it *also* represents 100%. Therefore, one swimmer (one block) represents 100% ÷ 25 = 4%.
So, 18 swimmers represent 18 · 4% = 72%.

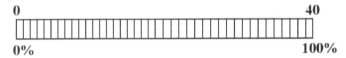

You can also simply write the fraction 18/25 as a percentage: 18/25 = 72/100 = 72%.

4. Fifteen percent of the 40 workers in a shop are over 50 years old. Now, think carefully. Which of the following are correct?

   a. 15/40 of the workers are over 50. **OR** 15/100 of the workers are over 50.

   b. 6 workers are over 50. **OR** 15 workers are over 50.

In problems 5-7, you can draw a diagram to help you solve the problem.

5. Justin gave away 70% of the 20 stuffed animals he had.
   How many does he have left?

6. Jerry painted 15 meters of fence out of the 25 meters that need to be painted.
   What percentage of the job did he do?
   (Round your answer to a whole percent.)

7. Marie wasted 30% of her $20 on candy.
   How much money does she have left?

8. How many percent of each figure is colored?

> **Example 2.** *How many percent of a 5-m tree is a tiny 28-cm sapling?*
>
> 1. Find out *what part* (what fraction) of a 5-m tree a 28-cm sapling is. We cannot compare the two unless we write the heights in the same units. Five meters is 500 cm. So, the 28-centimeter sapling is a 28/500 = 7/125 part of the 5-m tree.
>
> 2. Write 7/125 as a percentage. Using a calculator, 7 ÷ 125 = 0.056, or rounded to two decimals, 0.06. This is a *decimal.* As a percentage, 0.06 is 6%.

9. **a.** Evelyn is 1 m 4 cm tall and Mary is 1 m 57 cm tall.
   What percent of Mary's height is Evelyn's height?

   b. Jacqueline is 90% of the height of her father, who is 1 m 90 cm tall.
   How tall is Jacqueline?

10. Two college students, Peter and Jake, share a room. The rent is $450 per month, and they share the rent equally. Peter earns $900 a month, and Jake earns $1,350.

    a. Without calculating, determine which boy has to use a bigger part of his earnings to pay the rent. Explain your reasoning.

    b. Now find what percentage of his earnings each boy uses for the rent.

11. **a.** Without calculating, determine which is more money: 11% of $402 or 12% of $298? Explain how you figured it out.

    b. Estimate the *approximate* difference between the two amounts.

12. The Roberts family drove a 1,920-kilometer trip in four days. On the first day they drove 544 km, on the second day 448 km, on the third day 640 km, and on the fourth day the rest of the way.

    a. Find the average distance that they traveled per day.

    b. For each day, find what percentage of the total trip they drove.

    c. Suppose the family had divided the trip into four equal portions and driven the same distance each day. What percentage of the total trip would they have driven each day?

Finding the Total When the Percentage Is Known

> **Use a bar model to find the unknown total when you know the percentage and the quantity.**

Example 1. If 32 red marbles make up 4/5 of the total number of marbles, how many marbles are there in all?

Look at the bar model. We have drawn the marbles as divided into 5 equal "blocks." Four of those five blocks make up a total of 32 marbles. So, one block, or 1/5 of the marbles, is <u>8 marbles</u>. From that it is easy to calculate the total: 5 · 8 = 40 marbles.

The same reasoning works if the part of the marbles is given as a *percentage* instead of as a fraction:

Example 2. If 91 red marbles is 35% of the total number of marbles, how many marbles are there in all?

In the model, we need 100 little "blocks" with 35 of them colored (since 35/100 of the marbles are red.)

The calculation is done the same way: If 35 "blocks" or 35% make up 91 marbles, then one "block", or one percent, is 91 ÷ 35 = 2.6. Then, to find the total, simply multiply that number by 100: 2.6 · 100 = 260.

1. Margie gave away 40 marbles, which was 20% of the marbles that she had.
   How many marbles did Margie have at first?
   Hint: Instead of 100 blocks, you can use 5 blocks, each representing 20% or 1/5.

2. Emma cut down the amount of sugar in a recipe by 75%.
   Now, she uses only 1/2 cup of sugar.
   How much sugar did the recipe call for originally?
   Hint: Instead of 100 blocks, you can use 4 blocks, each representing 25%.

3. When Eric bought a guitar for $90, he used up 12% of the money he had.
   How much money did he have at first?

Example 3. A phone was discounted by 40% and now costs $72. What was the price before the discount?

The cost now, $72, represents **60%** of the original total—not 40%.

We can find 10% of the original price by dividing $72 ÷ 6 = $12. And from that, 100% of the price is 10 times that, or $120. If this confuses you, draw a bar model with 10 parts, each representing 10% of the original price.

4. A dress was discounted by 20%.
   The discounted price is $24.
   What was the price before the discount?

5. A concert ticket was discounted by 60%.
   The discounted price is $21.60.
   What was the original price?

6. Joe spent 72% of his money, and now he has $56 left.
   How much did Joe have to begin with?

7. Crystal spent 52% of her money and now she has $120 left.
   How much did she spend?

8. Uncle Jack raises two different breeds of cows on his farm. Of his cows, 28% are Black Angus and the rest are Hereford. If he has 420 Black Angus cows, how many Herefords does he have?

9. A survey found out that 16% of the people who had bought a certain brand of coffee grinder were unhappy with it. If there were 126 people who *were* happy with it, then how many people in total had bought that brand?

Puzzle Corner   One calculator is discounted by 30% and now costs $42.
                 Another is discounted by 25% and now it also costs $42.
                 Which calculator had the cheaper original price? How much cheaper?

Chapter 5 Mixed Review

1. Divide using long division in your notebook. Then, check your result. (Review of the Four Operations 1/Ch.1)

a. $339,427 \div 26 =$ _____ R _____ _____ . _____ + _____ = _____	**b.** $6,594 \div 145 =$ _____ R _____ _____ . _____ + _____ = _____

2. Compare and write **<** , **>** or **=**. (Powers and Exponents/Ch.1)

a. 659,000 ☐ 10^6	**b.** 10 billion ☐ 10^9	**c.** $10^6 + 10^2$ ☐ 1,001,000
d. 4^3 ☐ 3^4	**e.** 2^3 ☐ 3^2	**f.** $9 \cdot 10^4$ ☐ $2 \cdot 10^5$

3. Evaluate the expressions when the value of the variable is given. (Expressions, Part 1/Ch.2)

a. $150 - 7s$ when $s = 9$	**b.** $\dfrac{3 + x}{x}$ when $x = 5$

4. Write in simplified form an expression for the area
   and an expression for the perimeter of the shape.
   (Writing and Simplifying Expressions 2/Ch.2)

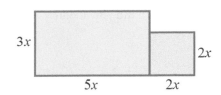

5. Simplify the expressions. (Writing and Simplifying Expressions 1/Ch.2)

a. $y + 7 + 3y$	**b.** $r \cdot r \cdot r \cdot 8$

6. Choose the expressions that have the value 6. (Review: Multiply and Divide Decimals Mentally/Ch.3)

a. $18 \div 3$ **b.** $1.8 \div 0.03$ **c.** $0.18 \div 0.03$ **d.** $1.2 \div 0.2$

e. $360 \div 6$ **f.** $3.6 \div 0.6$ **g.** $0.00036 \div 0.00006$ **h.** $0.9 \div 1.5$

i. $0.9 \div 0.15$ **j.** $0.009 \div 0.0015$ **k.** $0.0012 \div 0.002$ **l.** $0.0006 \div 0.0001$

7. One paper clip weighs 14 dg. They are sold in boxes of 200.   (Convert Metric Measuring Units/Ch.3)

   a. Calculate the weight of the box, in grams.

   b. If someone wanted 1 kg of paperclips,
     how many boxes would he need to buy?

8. Sandra gets paid $6 for every 15 minutes she works. Fill in the missing numbers to form equivalent rates.
   (Using Equivalent Rates/Ch.4)

$$\frac{}{5 \text{ min}} = \frac{\$6}{15 \text{ min}} = \frac{}{20 \text{ min}} = \frac{}{25 \text{ min}} = \frac{}{1 \text{ hr}}$$

9. The width and length of a rectangle are in a ratio of 1:7, and its
   perimeter is 120 mm. Find the rectangle's width and length.
   (Aspect Ratio/Ch.4)

10. On average, Gary makes a basket eight times out of every ten shots.
    How many baskets can he expect to make when he practices 25 shots?
    (Unit Rates/Ch.4)

11. Solve the equations. (Solving Equations/Ch.2)

a.	$312 = x + 78$	**b.**	$\dfrac{z}{2} = 60 + 80$	**c.**	$7y - 2y = 45$
	$=$		$=$		$=$
	$=$		$=$		$=$

12. A car travels with a steady speed of 39 kilometers per 30 minutes. Fill in the table.
    (Ratios and Rates/Ch.4)

Distance		39 km				
Time	10 min	30 min	50 min	1 hour	2 1/2 hours	3 hours

Review: Percent

1. Find a percentage of a number	2. A fractional part as a percentage
What is 60% of 300 kilometers? Calculate 0.6 · 300 kilometers = 180 kilometers. Or, using mental math, first calculate 10% of 300 kilometers, which is 1/10 of it, or 30 kilometers. Then multiply 6 · 30 kilometers = 180 kilometers. *Of the 15,400 workers in a city, 22% work in a steel factory. How many workers is that?* Calculate: 0.22 · 15,400 = 3,388 workers.	*What percent is 600 g of 2 kg?* Write the fraction $\dfrac{600 \text{ g}}{2{,}000 \text{ g}} = \dfrac{6}{20} = \dfrac{30}{100} = 30\%$. *One backpack costs $18 and another costs $29. What percentage is the price of the cheaper backpack of the price of the more expensive one?* Write the fraction $\dfrac{\$18}{\$29} = 0.6206... \approx 62\%$.
1. Change the percentage into a decimal. 2. Then multiply the number by that decimal. Alternatively, use mental math shortcuts for finding 5%, 10%, 20%, 25%, 50%, *etc.* of a number.	1. First write the fraction. Note that the two quantities in the fraction must both be in the same units: both grams, both meters, both dollars, *etc.* 2. Then convert the fraction into a decimal and finally a percentage.

1. Write as percentages, fractions and decimals.

a. _____% $= \dfrac{68}{100} =$ _____	**b.** 7% $= \dfrac{}{} =$ _____	**c.** _____% $= \dfrac{}{} = 0.15$
d. 120% $= \dfrac{}{} =$ _____	**e.** _____% $= \dfrac{224}{100} =$ _____	**f.** _____% $= \dfrac{}{} = 0.06$

2. Fill in the table. Use mental math.

percentage ↓ number →	6 100	90	57	6
1% of the number				
4% of the number				
10% of the number				
30% of the number				

3. A group of skaters consists of 15 girls and 5 boys.
   What percentage of the skaters are girls?

4. Write as percentages. You may need long division in some problems.
   If necessary, round your answers to the nearest percent.

   a. 3/4

   b. 2/25

   c. 1 5/8

5. Emma is 1 m 63 cm tall and Madison is 1 m 22 cm tall. How
   many percent is Emma's height of Madison's height?

6. A cheap chair costs $25. The price of another chair is 140% of that.
   How much does the other chair cost?

7. A bag has 25 green marbles and some white ones, too. The green marbles are 20% of the total.
   How many marbles are there in total? How many white marbles are there?

8. Andrew earns $2,000 monthly. He pays $540 of his salary in taxes.
   What percentage of his income does Andrew pay in taxes?

9. Which is cheaper, an $18 shirt discounted by 20%,
   or a $16 shirt discounted by 10%?

10. (*Challenge*) One square has sides 2 cm long, and another has sides 4 cm long.
    How many percent is the area of the smaller square of the area of the larger square?